Muddy Backroads
Stories from Off the Beaten Path

Muddy Backroads
Stories from Off the Beaten Path

edited by Luanne Smith
& Bonnie Jo Campbell

Lake Dallas, Texas

FIRST EDITION

Requests for permission to reprint material
from this work should be sent to:

Permissions
Madville Publishing
P.O. Box 358
Lake Dallas, TX 75065

Cover Design: Jacqueline Davis
Cover Art: Paul Kanevsky

ISBN: 978-1-956440-14-0 paperback,
ISBN: 978-1-956440-15-7 ebook
Library of Congress Control Number: 2022932007

Contents

Preface

Luanne Smith

There's this short story I taught for decades. Students loved it, no matter the years between its setting and their reality. Like classic rock music, T.C. Boyle's story, "Greasy Lake," reached across time and connected.

When writer and friend, Jodi Angel, and I started tossing around ideas for a new anthology, she came up with Muddy Backroads. I immediately thought of "Greasy Lake." We added the "Stories From Off the Beaten Path" to capture what we both had in mind, those stories that veer away from our comfort zones, away from what we know as routine or normal.

There's a line in "Greasy Lake," that takes us where we wanted these stories to go.

> Through the center of town, up the strip, past the housing
> developments and shopping malls, street lights giving way
> to the thin streaming illumination of the headlights, trees
> crowding the asphalt in a black unbroken wall: that wasthe
> way out to Greasy Lake.

Just as T.C. Boyle was inspired by Bruce Springsteen's "Spirit in the Night" for "Greasy Lake," I have always been inspired by Boyle's one-sentence ability to move us away from civilization to a place where anything can happen.

Muddy Backroads is the third anthology I have curated, and in all three, I have sought out stories and memoirs that take us to the edge. In an interview about the second anthology, *Taboos & Transgressions: Stories of Wrongdoings*, edited by me, Kerry Neville and Devi Laskar, the interviewer asked what drew me to such stories. I've been thinking about the answer to that question for a long time now. Yes, those stories and those writers are the ones I prefer to read. Dorothy Allison, Larry Brown, Richard Ford, Russell Banks, Jesmyn Ward, my co-editor for this anthology, Bonnie Jo Campbell. All of them take us away from what we know of civilization. But why am I drawn to these stories and memoirs?

"Because I always have been," doesn't sound like a real answer. But I was the kid who left our tiny Kentucky elementary school in third grade on a trip with my parents to New York City for Dad to attend a training session for his job. Upon return when I was asked to tell the class about New York City, I forgot all about the Statue of Liberty and the Empire State Building and told my classmates about seeing hippies (it was in the 1960's), about the drunk on all fours in Little Italy throwing up on the sidewalk, about the woman in the bus station riding the escalator up and down singing at the top of her lungs, about the waiter at the deli who only knew how to say, "Hello, may I help you?" in English. It was the individuals of NYC who caught my attention, the outsiders, the ones who did not quite fit, even in that big city.

Around that same time, I watched this movie on our little black and white TV. Television was still a fairly new thing, and my parents had no idea they needed to censor what I watched. So, I sat there on my own and watched Natalie Wood, Charles Bronson, and a young Robert Redford in a film version of Tennessee Williams' *This Property is Condemned*. I can't claim now that I completely understood all of what was going on in that story at that time, but I loved it. It was right up there with *101 Dalmations* as my favorite movie. I still love it—and all of Tennessee Williams' work.

So how do you explain to an interviewer something that probably requires years of professional therapy to understand? I prefer stories that don't pull punches. I prefer characters who are "off the beaten path." I prefer riding down that road past the shopping malls and finding myself in a place where anything can happen.

It was a pleasure to read the many stories submitted for consideration for *Muddy Backroads*. They took us so many places and off so many beaten paths. I want to thank Jodi Angel for brainstorming the theme with me for this book. Jodi had to step away from co-editing for personal reasons, but we still owe a lot to her for the existence of this anthology. I want to thank Bonnie Jo Campbell for co-editing with me. Who better to edit such a book? I want to offer a personal thanks to my friend, Dorothy Allison, who always encourages me, and I'm so happy to include her work here. Special thanks to Cat Smith and Kim Davis from Madville Publishing for all their hard, hard work and for supporting my visions, however dark they may be. Thanks, too, to Alan Heathcock, author of *Volt: Stories*, who is judging the unsolicited manuscripts within *Muddy Backroads* for cash prizes. Finally, I don't know how many times I indirectly thank T.C. Boyle in this foreword, but Mr. Boyle, what an inspiration your work is to me and my many creative writing students. Thank you hardly seems like enough.

Lastly, thank you to all the writers who are in the anthology and all who submitted work. Please, keep walking your own paths, writing your own stories, and taking us to all places where anything can happen.

—Luanne Smith

Foreword

Bonnie Jo Campbell

Like American painting, American writing often returns to landscapes, vistas where the names of flowers and birds and stars and makes and models of automobiles matter—before cars and trucks it was breeds of horses and temperaments of mules. These unpeopled places serve as proving grounds for our social selves and mirrors for our lonely American souls, and they give room and board to our twin longings for freedom and rootedness. When the problem is feeling lost at home, the solution is often a road trip. The stories in this book belong to this tradition of getting ourselves lost in order to find ourselves.

These stories are filled with weather and wildlife, Jesus and canned beer, motels and trailers and marijuana gardens. Some take us to other forms of wilderness, places we get lost while writing a story, while dealing with an icy stepmother, or negotiating with a ghost only we can see. These stories explore emotionally difficult places as well as physically challenging ones, spaces we must enter alone because the rules of the community do not apply. This is how protagonists end up in predicaments from which they (and *we*, by extension) can be saved only by their (*our*) own wits. In the wilderness, we have the freedom to sing loudly whatever we want, and our greatest fear is that what we sing doesn't matter.

On a personal note, I'm glad to see so many richly envisioned small-towns, so many fleshed-out rural characters. These are people who struggle against the elements in concrete ways that can serve as metaphors for the more abstract struggles we are working through on a daily basis. Anybody who doubts the importance of understanding small town and rural characters should notice that these places have given birth to our most recent populist political movement, a movement that many consider to be the dangerous to democracy, and that is why it behooves us to explore the isolated places where bitterness and anger brews and where firearms are plentiful.

I want to applaud the writers in this book for showing us what happens at the end of the road, what happens when folks reach the end of their ropes, when they are out on a limb with a handsaw. I want to thank Luanne Smith for brainstorming this project that allows us to explore some of the best-known American back roads voices and new voices from regions we have yet to discover, many of them working class voices. And I want to thank the readers of this book for believing in fiction writers as deliverers of truths and images that matter.

When I teach fiction writing, I ask my students *Why do we even need fiction?* We have poetry to explore emotional avenues, and we have non-fiction and journalism to hit us hard with life's surprising joys and injustices and to spur us to protest and celebration in the streets. We have memoirs to help us reflect upon myriad lives lived and examined. Still, I am certain that fiction can get at the difficult truths in a way those other forms cannot. Only fictional characters are allowed to honestly express the complexity of real human thoughts, the thoughts of the victims and the perpetrators, the dark and the light. Fiction is the most honest literary form, and therefore the most potent and most democratic

Please enjoy these lively, soulful stories we've chosen to include in this anthology from among dozens of other worthy tales. They will give you glimpses into backyards, gardens, great sweeping vistas and lonely aching hearts. Please get lost in these pages and try to find yourself, and when you do, take a good look in the mirror.

—*Bonnie Jo Campbell*

Muddy Backroads
Stories From Off the Beaten Path

Barrio Walden

Luis Alberto Urrea

Imagine my shock. I was living in Massachusetts for the first time. Adjusting. The first time I saw snow falling past my Somerville apartment window, I told a woman on the phone that a neighbor was on the roof shaking out a pillow. Not many snowstorms in my desertified homeland. The first time I saw ice on the sidewalk, I thought a prankster had smeared Vaseline on the bricks to watch businessmen fall down.

This old world was all new to me. I was manhandled by quotidian revelations, wrenched by the duende of Yankee cultural hoodoo. So when I realized I could walk over to Porter Square (where the porterhouse steak was first hacked out of some Bostonian cow) and catch a commuter train to Concord, to Walden freakin' Pond, I was off and running.

Perhaps I was a barrio Transcendentalist. Well, I was certainly one by the time I hit the San Diego 'burbs in my tweens. I loved me some Thoreau. "Civil Disobedience," right? What Doors fan couldn't get behind that? I also had copied passages of "Self Reliance" by Emerson and pasted them to my walls amid posters of hot rods and King Kong and John Lennon and trees. Even in the '70s, I was deeply worried about trees.

So I trudged to the T stop and went down to the suburban rail level and caught the Purple Line. I, and all the rambunctious Concord high school kids, were deeply plugged into our Walkmans. I was all Screaming Blue Messiahs and class rage, scribbling in my notebooks about rich bastards giggling self-indulgently and shrieking "Eau my GWOD!" at each other as they ignored the woods and the mangy deer outside. For me, it was a Disneyland train ride, all this stuff I had only experienced robotically before. I was imagining the ditch diggers from my old neighborhood tripping out over all this water. These goddamned New Englanders had water everywhere. And deer.

We pulled into Concord as if it were a normal thing, and I detrained and stepped into the Friendly's. At the time, if I could have had deep-tissue grafts of Americana I would have, and a striped-awning ice cream place where the happy lady called me "Deah" was just about the shiniest moment of my Americanness to date.

"I'm looking for Walden," I announced. "Pond." Helpful-like, as if she didn't know.

"Right out the door." Doah. "Go out and walk about a mile."

I drank some soda. She called it "tonic." And I was off. She didn't tell me I had to turn south. I turned north. And walked away.

Before we proceed much farther on our first New England early autumn country walk, before we grow dizzy with red maples actually turning red in a natural psychedelic blowmind, we might consider the dearth of what you might call "ponds" where I come from. To me, a pond was a muddy hole you could jump across, and it housed six or seven crawdads and some tadpoles. (My friend Mark put dead polliwogs in a jar with hand lotion and charged kids a nickel to look at "elephant sperm." We were guttersnipe naturalists.) When Thoreau said, "Time is but the stream I go a-fishing in," I thought I knew what he was talking about, though my stream was rain-shower runoff in an alley. I had been fishing exactly once in my life, and I felt guilt about the poor worm that came out of the water not only impaled on the hook but stiff as a twig.

So there I was, marching at a splendid pace! Away to Walden Pond! Or, as my homeboys would have spelled it, GUALDENG! Delighted by every tree! White fences! Orange and yellow and scarlet leaves! Concord thinned and vanished and I was suddenly among farms! Huzzah! Well-met, shrieking farm dogs threatening me! Bonjour, paranoiac farm wives hanging laundry and glaring at me from fields of golden, uh, barley! Eau my gwod! I saw stacks of lobster pots. I saw pumpkins. It was a shock to me that pumpkins grew somewhere. Next to lobster pots! And a red tractor to boot.

Behold the festive black-and-white New England moo-cow. Scenes bucolic and poetic—scenes the Alcotts might have penned. Sad autumn light, what a hipster pal in Harvard Square had called "Irish light," slanted through the trees to make everything tremble with the most delicious melancholy I have yet to see again. I was bellowing along to Sisters of Mercy: "Oh Marian, this world is killing me." Cows regarded me. Goths in paradise.

Right about then, I beheld it. In a field of mown hay. Next to a small house and a slanty barn. Walden Pond. It was about twenty feet across and surrounded by meditative heifers. I removed my headphones and went to the fence and leaned upon the topmost rail and communed with the transcendent. I wrestled with man's fate and the epic movements of the universe and the natural splendour of the Creator's delight in the temple of His Creation.

The farmer came out of his house and stared at me. I waved. He jumped in his truck and banged over ruts in his field. He wasn't smiling.

"I help you?" he shouted.

"Just looking at the pond," said I.

"What pond?"

"Walden Pond!"

"Jesus Christ!" he reasoned. He looked back at his cows. He looked at me. He looked at the cows. He said, "You're not from around here, are ya?"

"California," I said.

"That explains it."

What ho, my good fellow!

"You walked the wrong damned direction. It's about four mile that way."

I looked back, as though the great pond would reveal itself in the autumnal haze.

"Could you give me a ride?" I asked.

"Hell no!"

He smoked as he watched me trudge back toward Concord with a slightly less splendid cadence.

Yeah, whatever. Barking dogs. Screw you. Farm wives gawking. What's your problem? My feet hurt. Past Friendly's. Don't do me any favors, Deah. And south, out of town again, across the crazed traffic on the highway, and past a tumbledown trailer park and a garbage dump. What is this crap? Tijuana?

Gradually, I became aware of a bright blue mass to my right. A sea. A Great Lake. This deal wasn't a pond, man. Are you kidding? Who called this Sea of Cortez a pond?

Down to the water. A crust of harlequin leaves lay along the shore. It was dead silent. Thin wisps of steam rode the far shoreline. I squatted and watched and fancied myself living in a shack, smoking my pipe, scratching out one-liners with a quill, changing the world.

An ancient Dalmatian came along. He was stiff and arthritic, walking at an angle, grinning and making horking sounds. His tag said his name was Jason.

"Jason," I said. "I'm looking for Thoreau."

"Snork," he said, and headed out. I followed. We walked past cove and bog and found ourselves at Henry's stone floor. The cairn of stones left by travelers. I was glad my homeys did not see me cry over mere rocks.

The shack was about the size of my small bedroom back home in San Diego. I put my hand on the old pines and felt Henry's bark against my palm. Jason sneezed and thumped along to his own meditations. The pond moved in slow motion before us, Henry and me. A train rolled past the far trees like some strange dream.

Crows went from shadow to shadow, arguing.

Was it just me, or did I smell pipe tobacco burning?

I placed my stone on the cairn. I tipped my collar to my chin. Fall turned cold fast in those days. "Adios, Enrique," I said. Then I headed back to town for a hot cup of coffee and a ride home on a dark train.

Memory Stone

Siobhan Wright

My father's wife Cindy pats down the soil around hyacinths planted around a polished granite stone erected in memory of my sister, Lee, who disappeared two years ago. I don't like the stone. I don't like anything about it. For one, it reads *In Loving Memory of Leah Susan Porter.* No one calls my sister Leah. We call her *Lee.* The granite is gray. I didn't want a memory stone at all, especially not next to the Trinity Bible Church. I wanted to plant a tree, an oak tree, like the one that used to stand in a field behind our house, behind all the houses on our street. We hung out there. Not just Lee and me. Lots of kids. We called it, simply, *the tree.* I want to replace it because it once held Lee in its branches, but I'm too afraid to say so. Instead, I imagine Lee smoking a joint, contemplating the unlikely piece of granite, agreeing with my unspoken wishes, remarking "Assholes." Thin blue smoke escapes her lips as she dissolves in my imagination.

Cindy brushes off her jeans as she stands up. She's been kneeling on a yoga mat. She's clean and dry. "What do you think, Betsy?" she asks, digging for my approval. The memory stone was her idea. I push my glasses up to the bridge of my nose. "It makes her seem dead," I say. My father and Cindy exchange a look that is a full conversation about me. They think I'm in denial, that I need spiritual intervention, that I need to accept the Lord Jesus Christ as my savior. I gaze across the road at the purple and yellow field that bursts with promise and wonder how I will make it through a candlelight service tonight at a church that Lee never attended with people who don't know her, but who will come to pray for her because they know other addicts. I don't think of Lee as an addict.

My father says, "Let us bow our heads." He joins hands with Cindy and my 10-year-old brother. They wait for me to complete the circle. I do. But I can't bring myself to bow my head or close my eyes. "Help us, Jesus, to accept our loss," he says, beginning a prayer that's not mine. A gust of wind, cold as snow, bends the hyacinths and lifts Cindy's blond ponytail from her shoulder.

Lee called Cindy *Malibu Barbie* behind her back because she's tan even in the winter. She's barely old enough to be my mother. Lee didn't like Cindy. I like Cindy more than I like my father. I know she tries, too hard sometimes, but she tries to be parental without pretending to be my mother. My mother lives in a motel room at the other end of town. I realize during the prayer that the field across the street is connected to the field behind our house where the tree grew. It's a big field.

"Amen," my father says. "Amen," Cindy and Liam echo. I say nothing. I'm still thinking about the size of the field. They're all looking at me. The pressure to say something bears down on me, and I blurt out, "Liam and I are late for school." My father's eyes narrow. His jaw flexes. "Let's go," he says. The contempt that surfaces on his face is familiar and puts me right back in the bunkbeds I shared with Lee, back when we curled up together on the bottom mattress, listening to hurled insults to see if my mother would step over the line. If she stepped over the line, we would hear her hit the wall or the floor or a piece of furniture.

"Betsy?" Cindy asks. I snap out of it. My father strides across the flat lawn in front of the church. His steps are too long. I watch until he reaches the minivan, which straddles two spaces in the otherwise empty parking lot. Cindy rolls up the yoga mat. I head across the grass with Cindy and Liam. All at once my foot sinks into a soft spot in the lawn and ice-cold water soaks my canvas tennis shoe. "Shit," I say. I try to tiptoe out of the muck. By the time I reach the parking lot both shoes are ruined. I'm splattered in mud and shivering.

"We'll take you home to change," Cindy offers. My throat burns. I haven't missed a moment of school since Lee disappeared. I know without being able to say how that if she comes to find me, she will go to the school. I stare at my soaked feet and cannot speak. If I speak, my voice will crack. If my voice cracks, I will cry. If I cry, I will sound like I'm dying. "It's okay to be late sometimes," Cindy says. I nod my head and get into the van. The door closes automatically.

My father drives toward town. The elementary school isn't far. It sits on the outskirts of town. It's a flat town with brick streets and a fountain in the center. There's no water in the fountain. Ever. The sky stretches like an umbrella, horizon to horizon, but beautiful skies make the town even more grungy. It's no wonder that Lee got away from here. Even the movie theatre is closed. We pull up in front of the elementary school. There are no swings on the swing set. "Bye, Ma!" Liam says to Cindy, flashing a defiant look at me. He has wavy red hair and looks like our mother. "I'll see you after school," I say.

He catches my eye. "Who cares!" he snaps. It stings, but he's ten and confused. I know that when he sees me in the afternoon when the school bus pulls up outside our house, he will have forgiven me for not going along with the prayer circle, for not wanting a memory stone. Cindy whispers something into his ear that I don't quite hear as she hands him his lunch box outside the van. "Bye, Betsy," he says without looking at me. As my father pulls away, I watch Liam avoid the cracks in the sidewalk so that he doesn't break his real mother's back. He misses her.

We pull out onto the road again. Up ahead is the motel where my mother lives. No one says a word until we pass it. My mother's old Honda isn't outside her room, number 33. "I don't know how that woman lives with herself," my father says to Cindy, but it's loud enough for me to hear. I hate this lobbying effort, the indirect way he asserts that he's a better parent than my mom. I'm glad when Cindy doesn't flinch, doesn't move, doesn't look at the rundown place my mother calls home. As we pass, I have this weird feeling, like a gumball of pain falls from my throat and through my chest all the way to my stomach. I wish that I was angry. I wish that I wasn't grateful for knowing my mom's address and phone number. She sends me a kiss and a hug, XO, by text message every night at 10 o'clock. My father doesn't know this. It's a secret.

My mother's love for me is real but difficult to explain. She's trying to get herself together. To recover, I guess. She used to work at the factory before it closed. Then she had no job. Now she cleans houses closer to the city. She's embarrassed by her life. This is just how I understand things, though. When Lee was fifteen, she was caught selling pot in the girls' lavatory next to the school office. Believe it or not, it's the most active drug market in town, at least now that the tree is gone. Mom wept and packed a bag—all over pot that Lee sold.

"Where are you going?" Lee asked.

"I don't know," my mother said, her face raw and pink like a slice of jumbo bologna.

"I wasn't selling anything," Lee insists. "I just fronted them money, and they were paying me back for pot. It's legal."

"It's not legal," my mother said flatly.

"Just ground me or something," Lee begged.

"I'll leave that to your father."

"No," Lee replied.

When my mother walked out the front door with her suitcase, my father was sitting on the couch. "You'll have to cook dinner," he yelled.

"Fuck off," Lee spat, spinning on her heel. Her auburn hair swept around her like a cape, and her black suede boots clicked on the parquet tiles all the way to our room.

"Where the Hell do you think you're going?" he bellowed after her. The sound of his voice shook me up inside. I know that I'm making him sound like a bad person. He's just loud. He was so loud when he yelled at Lee that it felt like the windows would crack. Lee answered him by slamming the bedroom door. My father looked at me, his face twisted and red, and said, "Don't you say a word."

There were no words in me. I opened the Betty Crocker Cookbook and followed the recipe for macaroni and cheese. I couldn't get the look of his face out of my head. Liam must have been at a friend's house. I don't remember to be honest. I hope Liam wasn't even there. He could have been hiding under his covers.

Not long after my mother left to live at the motel, my dad accepted the Lord Jesus Christ as his personal savior at the mall near the city. There are no clothing or shoe stores in our town anymore, even though some of the signs for them are still up. The storefronts are empty. Anyhow, I had outgrown my shoes. Dad sat down on a bench under an indoor tree, near a water fountain with wish pennies in it. Water droplets sparkled in the air. "You've got thirty minutes," he said, tapping his watch. It was a Saturday afternoon in November.

"He's fucking miserable," Lee said to me under her breath, pulling me by the hand. She had his credit card. She was in charge of the shoe purchase, even though I was plenty old enough to scan the card and punch in the pin number.

"Your eyes are red," I told her. She pulled a bottle of eyedrops from her jacket pocket, dropped her head back, and squeezed the bottle. "I stay stoned so that I don't kill him," she said, wryly. It was around that time that we heard Reverend Bob's voice, liquid and warm and hopeful. I wanted to see him and pulled Lee through the crowd. He had silver hair and wore a black turtleneck. "The Lord is your savior," he announced. "That means nothing until you understand it. The Lord saves."

I loved that word. *Saved*. I loved that word when spoken by Reverend Bob. It warmed me up, and for a moment I could breathe better. Some words do that to me.

"Come be saved by the Lord Jesus Christ," he solicited, and I wanted to be saved.

"We've got twenty minutes," Lee said. The clock began to tick in my head again. Lee and I rode the escalator to the second floor, and Reverend Bob became smaller and smaller. "Don't fall for mall preachers," Lee counseled. "Religion is an addictive drug." I laughed. That was a funny statement coming from her. We went inside a shoe store, and I ran my finger down a black suede boot. "No," she said. "Dress like you. You'll be more comfortable." She was right. I am not dainty. I don't have fine bones and moist skin and thick auburn hair like Lee. She's so striking that no one ever forgets her, and that bothers me. Because no one has seen her in two years. No one. Her eleventh-grade school picture was published on Facebook and went all around the world. That photo was forwarded over a hundred thousand times. Someone at the police station monitors the responses. Maybe they've stopped by now. I don't know. I got off Facebook. You wouldn't believe what people write about girls who disappear. Mean words.

I am easy to forget. My name doesn't stick. My hair is dark and thin. I wear glasses. I'm a big girl but not fat. That's hard to describe. I wear a size 9 shoe. That day in the mall, I bought brown leather ankle boots with heavy tread. Lee said, "No one will fuck with you in those boots." They're fierce, the first pair of shoes that told Lee's friends at the tree that I was cool, one of them, even if I didn't party. I wore them out of the store and went to find Lee who had wandered out the door after paying with Dad's card. She was waiting outside, looking over the railing down on Reverend Bob's recruitment scene. She raised her eyebrows and said, "You won't believe this one." She lifted her chin to direct my attention downward. My father was behind a velvet rope, kneeling next to Cindy. We didn't know her yet, of course. To be honest, I only looked at my father. I thought, "He must like that word too." *Saved.*

All the people kneeled in front of Reverend Bob and then stretched their hands out in front of him, as if they were going to kiss the ground. My father is a big man. The crack of his butt showed a little bit. I flinched. Lee pulled her phone out and took a picture and sent it to her friends, I guess, with LMFAO under it. I was embarrassed for my dad, a new feeling. "He's gonna give up whisky and beer for religion," Lee said. And she was right. That's exactly what happened. I watched Lee scan the crowd, looking for our mother's features on every stranger's face, a game we played called "Are you my mother?" It's a line from a book she read to us when we were kids. Every time we thought we saw our mother in a public place, one of us would say to the other *the kitten or the hen or the cow is not our mother* and then Lee followed up with *Bitch!* The lights and the people in the mall seemed to grow louder, brighter. Lee bit her lower lip. Her high had lost its electricity. She was tired. "You ready?" I asked, and she nodded. We headed down the escalator, and I listened to the roaring water fountain.

My father pulls into our driveway and throws the van into park. Cindy and I jerk forward. I lurch out of my memory. He turns in his seat before I can escape and says, "Would you please say *something*? Cindy has knocked herself out getting this memorial together."

"It's okay," Cindy protests. It's almost a relief to see him this way again, angry and raw and real. Something shifts inside me. I don't have a word for it. He went on about the memory stone and the flowers and the candles and the invitations. She even sent one, my father says, to my mother. I didn't know that.

"Sorry," I say. It's more of a reflex.

"It's okay, Bets," she says. She has started to call me that. *Bets.* I'm trying to like the sound of that word but, to be honest, I just don't. But I nod at her all the same. I say to my dad, "I'll walk to school." But I'm thinking something different. I'm not going. They drive away, leaving me with soaking wet feet in the driveway. Since Lee left, I imagine her inside before I open the door. I imagine that she is sitting on the sofa with a bowl of popcorn or on the back porch smoking a cigarette. The first few weeks after she was gone were the worst. I went from room to room in the house just to keep imagining her around the next corner. Today, I don't do that. I just go inside and take off my wet sneakers without even untying them. My boots, the ones I bought at the mall, have dirty socks stuffed into them, and I sit down in the little entryway on the white bench, décor that Cindy added to our house. After I have tied the red laces, I close my eyes. I don't imagine Lee. I imagine the tree, the one that sat with crooked arms and bony fingers at the end, waiting to hold us all again. I want it back.

I head outside to the little shed next to our garage where my mother's gardening tools are still stored. I grab a shovel. I walk with the shovel against my shoulder like it's a loaded weapon. I know these fields well. I know that acorns fell for years from the tree, a tree I can see like a photograph if I close my eyes. My father cut it down after Lee overdosed on heroin. I heard her gagging in her sleep. She was on her bunk. Her eyes were turned back in her head. I screamed for my dad. I screamed until ambulance lights appeared in my bedroom window. I saved her. She just never came home. I wonder if she knows the tree is gone.

When the hospital called and said that she had checked herself out before they had a chance to get her to the psych ward, we waited. Even my mom came over. She admired Cindy's bench. Cindy made hot tea with teabags. When my father couldn't take the waiting anymore, I guess, he got his gas-powered chainsaw and marched across these very fields. In his mind, Lee was hooked on drugs because of a tree. His reasoning was gnarled, but I understood it in a way. I just didn't agree. All at once, we heard him start up the chainsaw. A black plume streamed into the air like an SOS signal. The limbs fell to the earth, one by one, with a thud I could feel in my feet. By the time my father finished, he was surround by teenagers, kids on bikes, and our neighbors, everyone knowing that our family had turned *troubled*. That's a word I hate. *Troubled*. Sap oozed from the stump, and Dad left behind a wake of sawdust and scattered logs and his former life. The thing is, everyone still gathers in the same place, at the stump, but they still call it *the tree*.

I miss it. It wasn't super big like the ones that are pictured on the internet when you search "oak tree," but it's the tree we learned to climb. We sat in its arms. I am determined to plant a new one, determined to find a tree that has sprouted from an acorn left behind. I know what the saplings look like. I walk along the path, looking for saplings. Off in the distance, two girls are leaping through the fields toward me, acting like five-year-olds. "Bet-SEE," I hear one of the girls call. "Bet-SEE!" Their hands are cupped around their mouths as they yell. They should be in school. I don't want to say their names and get them into trouble, but I know them. We're not friends exactly, but we used to trick-or-treat together. And, anyhow, Lee practically made me famous with high school kids, like I'm related to some bad ass and must be bad ass too. I'm not.

I find a little sapling. Its trunk is the size of a pencil. I sink the shovel too close to its roots and feel them snap. "Damn," I say. The girls are tripping over themselves and fighting fits of laughter to get to me. Every few feet one of them doubles over with a belly laugh, but finally one girl gets close, throws her arms back, and cries, "I found BET-SEE!" Her pupils seem as large as dimes to me, her cheeks the color of watermelon. She doesn't know how cold she is. High as a kite. She suddenly laughs and then the laughter turns off like a tap. "Come here," she says. I bend down to her until I feel the warmth of her breath on my face. She slides two fingers into my mouth before I have a chance to understand why. "Swallow. It's acid. We're tripping our assess off." Her fingers linger on my tongue. "Wow," she says. "Your mouth is, like, so warm."

It's too late. I've already swallowed. I know I'll have to trip on acid now. "How long will this last?" I ask, starting to panic. I don't do drugs. "Six," the girl says.

"Six hours?" I ask, adding up time in my head. I won't be down before Liam gets off the bus. Still, I am determined to find a tree and replant it. "Take this," I tell the first girl, giving her the shovel. I squat down to look through the grasses for another sapling. They're hard to find without leaves. Plus, they die. I asked my science teacher why. He theorizes that the winters are too wet and cold, and the summers too dry and hot. "They have to be watered," he told me.

I think I've found another sapling, and I signal to the girls to bring the shovel. They carry it like pall bearers and tell me that they stole the acid from one of their fathers. "Wow," I say. I'm not impressed.

"What are you doing?" one of the girls asks, like it's a conspiracy.

"I'm going to grow another tree," I tell them.

"You can do that?" they ask, like I have a superpower.

"Yes," I say. They are quiet and look at me like I'm Reverend Bob or something. They can see that I'm angry, that I didn't want to trip with them. I take the shovel and cut around another sapling, starting the dig further out from the base of the spindle-sized trunk. I dig up oak tree saplings for what feels like hours. My hands are blisters and ripped. I don't feel them. My head swims when I stand up straight. I have six decent saplings so far. The girls have become my tree disciples and have laid them out side by side, in order of height. One of the girls says, "They're beautiful." Only they're not. Or they aren't beautiful to me. They aren't even trees yet. But I'm glad not to be alone because I feel weird. The two girls have muddied the knees of their jeans looking at the saplings.

Then I dig the holes all around the stump. Once on a field trip, I learned that new trees sometimes connect to the roots of dead ones that are still somehow alive underground. I don't really understand the biology, but it fills me with hope that one of the saplings will survive. When I gaze out at the flat earth, it looks like I'm underwater. Tripping doesn't make me laugh. It makes me dig holes. I dig them big. My mother taught me that. I know that I should put stones in the bottom, but I don't have any. The girls help me plant the saplings. We put seven in the ground.

When we finish, the sun is low in the sky. Liam's bus has come and gone. Dinner dishes are being rinsed. People are probably getting dressed for the service at Trinity Bible Church. The girls are kneeling with me on the ground. We have made a circle of trees. We have packed soil around the roots. I stand up on the stump when we're done. "Listen to me," I call out to the umbrella sky. I am talking to Lee but disguising it. I am talking to the tree my father cut down, too. Honestly, maybe I'm just babbling, but words are coming from me. The girls sit and listen to me. "I will resurrect you," I cry. "I will save you."

The girls lift their white, cold hands into the air, like they will lay hands on me, like we're at church or something, and suddenly I feel myself rising, up and up, to the highest branches of the oak tree that once grew in this place. I can see the whole town spreading out along the main road. My mother's Honda is parked at the motel. The water fountain has water in it, and it sparkles in the light from a streetlamp. Liam tosses a coin into the fountain. He makes a wish that will come true. My mother brushes her hair in front of a mirror and applies make-up. The sidewalk to the church is lined with candles. The little flames burn brightly, illuminating the letters so precisely carved in the polished granite. But Lee is not in this vision, this hallucination. And I understand for the first time that I will never see her again. Down the highway, a tractor trailer blasts its horn.

Where To Buy Your Weed

Misty Skaggs

Her trailer was a ripe patch of excess, bloomed conspicuously at the base of a cliff on the edge of a bone dry, Baptist county in East Kentucky. There were always at least two or three dogs sunning themselves near the front steps. The half-acre around it was decorated haphazardly with a half dozen busted toilets turned planters. Mary Jack had filled them to the brim with rich bottom soil and planted sturdy annuals that burst forth bright colors, overflowing come springtime. And some nights you could hear her racket from a ridge over. Never music, just barking dogs and the strained voices of lonely people seeking solace over the air waves. Her regular customers learned to lean in when she hollered them across the threshold and into her home. They learned to brace themselves against the blast of cackling hosts crackling onto the hillbilly breeze via AM radio. The regulars, they planted their feet against decibel after decibel blaring through the stacks of secondhand speakers that towered and teetered close to the drooping, water-stained ceiling. If you were a brand new customer naively on the hunt for a quality buzz, it could be downright overwhelming.

Mary Jack herself was too much—too big, too loud, too self-assured, too self-righteous. In the history of her whole life, nobody ever called her a people person. She'd answer the door in a muu-muu splattered with crusty, sausage gravy and tacky floral print. She'd tell you how Jesus don't mind pot, but you better stay away from that ol' Detroit dope. She conducted most all her business out of the kitchen. There was always an abundance of food bubbling over on the stove and her rumbling old refrigerator was always stocked with leftover smells and cold beer. The mismatched canisters lining the counter tops were stuffed full of product. On the rare occasion she wasn't cooking when you'd show up to score, she'd take your money all flopped out and sweating across the queen size bed crowded into the built-on, back room of the mobile home. And she'd produce a thirty bag or a sixty bag or even a whole ounce or two out from under the folds of her dress. Or maybe out from under the folds of her fleshy body. Nobody ever dared to question the hygienic aspect once they realized that sticky, hairy bud smelled even stronger and danker than the dealer.

No one knew where she kept her crop, but she gave the living room over to the house plants. The ivy grew up over the arms of the couch and she warned guests to avoid the moldy Lazy Boy. Not for the sake of their pretty, clean clothes or pretty, clean lungs. Because once, the rotting plaid armchair had belonged to her Mommy, and now it belonged to the rosary vine. Her favorite. Her Mommy's favorite. Mary Jack kept the room cool and dark so that the thick, durable foliage of the rosary vine shone, reflecting the light of a single lamp that faked sunshine. And the blossoms were back lit, flickering red and wavering like candles at the base of a shrine to homegrown botany and the holy mother. Everybody on this side of the state knew she was thanking the good Lord for her green, green thumb.

Sebou Party

Paula Younger

At the Coptic Catholic seminary, Susan waited for the intermittent wireless connection called 'brown cow' to appear so she could ride its weak signals and talk to her husband. He appeared via webcam in their baby room. He had taken down the camel pictures that had hung in his room as a child. His deep blue eyes had bags beneath them. "It looks so bare there," he said. White paint chipped off from the seminary's cement ceiling and walls. The lack of decoration, except for Susan's English/Arabic Bible and her travel alarm clock, comforted her, as did her rock-hard twin-size bed that had no room for him. At first, she saw the bareness and hard surfaces as a type of penance, but she knew that wasn't true when she saw her husband in their comfortable house looking lost and haggard against those bright yellow walls. Maybe her summer in Cairo was meant to punish both of them.

"Are you going to come home?" he asked.

"Where else would I go?" But Susan imagined herself floating in the Dead Sea, where some of the other teachers talked about visiting after the summer session ended. A few months ago a family had lost their toddler on the Jordan side, but he had bobbed over to Israel, sunburned but unharmed. It was nearly impossible to drown in those saline waters. Susan wanted to dive into that water, daring it to swallow her. She would wear goggles to protect her eyes from the salt and her hands would dig into the mud at the bottom and test if that buoyant water could push her back out.

Susan checked her watch and said, "I have to go. Nader's taking me to a party."

Her husband frowned. "He's a seminarian, right?"

19

"Was. They kicked him out."

"For what?"

Instead of using the excuse Nader told her—too much time in the computer room—she went with the more salacious rumor the other seminarians spread. "Someone spotted him outside one of those cheap hotels with a girl. I've got to go."

Nader decided he was Susan's guide. She paid for the taxi rides and entrance fees, he showed her around Cairo. She emailed pictures of the two of them at the pyramids and Ibn Tulun mosque, hoping to worry her husband, just a bit.

Susan shut off the computer, knowing at some point she would have to acknowledge her husband was hurt too. She pulled out the twenty-week ultrasound pictures from her Arabic/English Bible. The ultrasound tech had typed "Hi, Mom & Dad!!" on the one of their baby kicking his legs. In another picture their baby faced the camera. The lines of his skeleton face were clear, as if he knew what she was about to do to him and he wanted to ask for a pardon.

Susan stepped over a blood soaked sidewalk in Shrabaya, on the outskirts of Cairo. Small red pools dribbled into the street. Nader stepped around the blood, protecting his cheap leather sandals, the type Susan imagined Jesus wore and that were sold all over Egypt for five pounds, thirty for foreigners. Nader hadn't led her wrong on any of his outings, but still Susan asked, "Should I be concerned about the blood?"

"Do not worry. It is a sacrifice for the Sebou."

"What type of party requires a sacrifice?"

"Very important. This celebrates a baby being alive for seven days."

Susan had agreed to Nader's invitation to witness an important cultural event in an Egyptian's life, whether Christian or Muslim, unaware it had anything to do with babies. "I should go back," she said. "I have to get up early to teach."

But their taxi had disappeared. Children took over the street, shutting off traffic with their soccer game. They played beneath an outdated billboard of Mubarak, Egypt's president who had held power for the past twenty-seven years under emergency rule. The color was faded, baked in the hot sun.

Nader smiled. "You must come. They are expecting you." He used the word 'must' too often and she wanted to educate him about what that word meant. He took her hand and said, "Come, come."

If Susan didn't have to see the baby, she might be okay. But on the third floor a woman stood outside an opened apartment door holding a baby boy with chubby legs and a full head of black hair. Arabic music blared into the hallway. The woman wore a blue dress with matching electric blue eye shadow. A younger looking version of the mother stood next to her in a pink top with complementing eye shadow. The baby stared at Susan with large, unblinking eyes.

Nader pointed to the woman in blue and said, "This is Umm Josef and her sister, Mariam."

He held Susan's arm and introduced her. Mariam said, "Like Mubarak's wife, Suzanne." Throughout Egypt Susan's name was changed to Suzanne, the president's British wife.

Susan shouted above the din of the frenetic Arabic music blaring over the stereo, "*Mabrouk!*" Arabic for 'congratulations,' and fortunately a word with sounds Susan was used to. Nader had coached her how to say it on their taxi ride. She wrote it down phonetically in her little notebook, next to the other phrases he taught her.

Nader added, "*Mash'allah*." He winked at her. "You must not forget about God." A person should not praise a baby or child without adding the phrase "*mash'allah*." 'By the will of God' was a reminder that only God was in control. Anyone could lose anyone, anything, at any time. Susan knew that all too well and hadn't prayed since she and her husband had left the hospital.

Susan smiled at Umm Josef and said, "He is *gamila*." Beautiful probably wasn't the right word to use when praising a boy, but Susan couldn't think of another Arabic word. She worried about looking too closely at the baby. Umm Josef might think Susan was giving him the evil eye or looking at him with envy, and she was. She longed to kiss his dimpled elbows. During the ultrasound, Susan's baby had been a mix of washy alien looking things. Her doctor had pointed out his scrotum and announced they were having a boy. Susan's husband joked that they couldn't have a son because he didn't know how to fix cars or appliances. But then the doctor looked closer at the screen and said, "This doesn't look right."

Umm Josef smiled and said, "You are welcome." She kissed Susan's right cheek and then her left one. Her aggressive belly bumped against Susan's stomach. Susan had felt substantial when she was pregnant, as if she were more than herself. When she boarded the plane to Cairo a month ago, her breasts leaked, despite wearing a tight bra to cease the dripping, like the doctor recommended. Susan didn't have breast pads. Mothers carried those. Each day at the seminary Susan woke up at 4:30 and ran around the dirt field where the seminarians played soccer in the afternoons. She hoped to trick her body into forgetting that it had been pregnant, but her breasts refused to deflate. She covered her legs in track pants in case someone in the nearby apartments was awake and could see her, despite the intense heat. The nearby mosque's mournful call to prayer swallowed her in its sound. She imagined a man in the minaret, solitary, keeping her company, even though the call to prayer was probably a recording.

On their way into the apartment, Susan asked Nader, "Why is she called mother of Josef?"

"So no one can curse her. If a man tries, he will have to say 'mother of Josef.' Her name is safe. The curse can not find her." He could be joking, but in Egypt it was an honor to be a mother, and it was the ultimate honor to be the mother of a boy. He represented the men that will protect the women of the family. The larger the family was in Egypt, the more protection you had. Really, it wasn't that different in America. Susan's big, ungainly Catholic family was like an army. One Thanksgiving when she was six, a group of boys started pulling her hair and telling her she couldn't use the swings. Before she could react, her siblings and cousins descended. Susan appreciated the security of a group, even though it was just she and her husband at home.

In the cramped apartment, women sat on chairs lined against the walls, forming a square around a group of dancing women. A few men were in attendance. During her time in Egypt, Susan wondered where the women were. They seemed tucked out of sight. She longed to talk to them after her days of teaching English to male priests-in-training. But in this apartment, Susan feared she might be kicked out. The seminarians, priests, Nader, and the other English teachers thought Susan was a nice woman who volunteered to travel to Egypt in her friend's place. Her childhood friend from Catholic school had spent the past five summers teaching English in Egypt but had to cancel after her mother's heart attack. None of the women in this room knew about Susan's pregnancy and what had happened to her baby boy.

As in each Egyptian home Susan had visited with Nader, a picture of Jesus hung on the wall, once again the white, blond, blue-eyed Jesus instead of a more Middle-Eastern-looking one, which Susan had seen once in a small church and kept hoping would reappear. She wanted the people and churches to feel authentic, a hearkening back to early Christianity and closer to the heart of the original church. The white Jesus seemed false, as if the Christian Egyptians had followed someone else's story without realizing it. In this picture, Mary, Jesus' vigilant mother, was absent. Susan sat beneath it and tucked her feet under her chair so she wouldn't trip the dancers.

Mariam handed Susan a plate of grisly meat and said, "I'm sorry we don't have more to offer. We already ate."

Susan took a bite of the rubbery meat and forced herself to swallow, knowing that meat was an honor. On English menus in Cairo, the sections were labeled 'meat' and 'chicken.' The few times Susan ate meat it tasted like the animals had hard lives and were killed right before they would have died anyway. She tasted their exhaustion

Then Susan remembered the blood-soaked sidewalk. She took a couple bites, crumpled a napkin above the meat, and then eased the plate beneath her chair.

The dancing women shook their hips, like Latin dancing, but even more frenzied. They spun each other around, planted their feet, shook their hips, and clapped their hands. The best ones kept shimmying their hips and it reminded Susan of belly dancing. A few men sat in chairs. The first time Susan saw men and women intermixed. Nader sat a few seats away, ready to act as translator.

Mariam smiled at Susan, like she expected something. Susan smiled back, hoping to make up for any accidental offence by looking nice and enthusiastic, silently apologizing for the meat beneath her chair. She said loudly, above the music, "I've never been to a party like this!"

Mariam tilted her head. "You do not celebrate child's birth?"

"We have a party before the baby is born. It's called a baby shower. Friends and family bring gifts and eat food."

Mariam frowned. "That is bad luck. Seven days after birth, that is good, but even then, *mash'allah*." She looked up at the ceiling, as if God waited there.

Susan fidgeted. She had asked her husband to wait. She wanted to hold their baby in her arms before decorating the room. But her husband created a list of favorite boys' and girls' names, a spreadsheet detailing items their baby would need, and cleaned out their office for the baby's nursery, as if he could control something as uncontrollable as birth. Their former office was now painted yellow and had a crib, dressing table, stroller, and the one item Susan allowed herself to buy, a black onesie that said, "The cat hates me." While she was pregnant, her husband carried everything for her, cleaned out the litter boxes, walked their dog, started cooking, even gave back rubs. But after they left the hospital, he began working later, sleeping longer, barely meeting her eyes over the few meals they shared.

Her friend called with the offer to go to Cairo and said, "You need to get away from that house." Susan had the airline miles and the school year had ended for her junior high kids. At dinner she gave her husband a printout of her flight itinerary. He asked, "What am I supposed to do?" She said, "Whatever you want." He could go to work and forget, but Susan's body was a reminder of what she had lost.

A teenage girl with green eye shadow sat down on the other side of Susan. She motioned to Susan's clothes and said, "Your clothes, delicious. Your hair, delicious."

Mariam introduced the green-eye-shadowed girl. "My younger sister, Asteer."

Asteer looked at Susan's brown espadrilles and clapped her hands. "Your shoes, delicious!"

Susan's red toenails peeked through the open tip of her wedged espadrilles, something the head priest declared improper. But another teacher at the seminary had painted Susan's toenails. She said Susan was too young and pretty to frown so much and she thought the nail polish might brighten her up. Besides, Susan wore long gypsy skirts, long-sleeved linen tops, careful not to show knees or shoulders or elbows in this insufferable heat. She wore her wedge espadrilles instead of flat sandals to keep from tripping over her skirts. The smaller her belly became, the longer her skirts seemed. These Coptic Catholic women wore their hair down, and their t-shirts and jeans tight, despite the summer heat. Susan felt dull next to these women in their vibrant tops and matching eye shadows. The dramatic colors would look clownish on Susan's pale skin. These women were peacocks and she was a lump of mozzarella cheese. Susan turned her head and dabbed on her pink lip-gloss with plumper, another gift, to give herself a little oomph.

Mariam and Asteer stared and said, "Oooh! *Gamila!*"

Most of the women did not wear lipstick, and definitely not gloss. Susan offered Mariam and Asteer the gloss, not sure how to warn about the plumper.

Mariam giggled and held her hand to her mouth. "It tickles." Nicer than saying it stung.

Susan took the bobby pins out of her flattened hair and shook her hair loose. The familiar weight brushed against her shoulders. When Nader took Susan around Islamic Cairo, he double-checked the scarf was tight on her head. Susan tried to restrain her hair, but tendrils escaped and her forehead slid into view. Nader pulled on her curls and laughed when they sprung back in place. At the largest mosque, she headed for the main doors, but he ushered her to a small, side entrance. Susan followed the women into a room that felt like a closet compared to the men's spacious area. Nader waved and smiled from his side, as if this was a funny joke. Susan stared at the men through the screen. They bowed and prayed, some slept on the cool marble floor, a break from the outside heat. She imagined her husband among those men, solemn and sad and removed and out of her reach.

Mariam asked Susan with a smile, "You look for husband?"

"I have one."

"Where is he?"

"In the United States."

"It's okay to travel without him?"

"Sure, sometimes it's good to be without the men in your life." Mariam's forehead crinkled. Susan added, "He misses me, but he's happy I'm having fun."

Mariam brightened. "That is wonderful!" Such a different reaction from the seminarians who couldn't believe her man would allow her to travel without him. But the seminarians were jealous of her excursions with Nader. Most were from Upper Egypt and had not seen the Pyramids at Giza. Susan toured them twice.

Nader said, "Here, men say that they will be a good husband and woman can spend time with family and friends, but then she marries and he won't let her go anywhere."

Susan said, "We call that bait and switch. You say one thing and then do another."

"Bait and switch?" Nader pulled out his pen and notebook, filled with American sayings and euphemisms, which wouldn't be much help with the more common British tourist. Since he couldn't become a priest, Nader decided he would be a tour guide.

Mariam glanced at Susan and said, "Your husband must miss you. You're very far away. You talk to him?"

Susan sat up straighter. "We try. Are you married?"

Mariam blushed. "*Insha'allah*, I will become a nun. God will be my husband. He is the best husband. Most devoted and kind."

Umm Josef and her blue eye shadow approached, arms outstretched with baby Josef. She handed him to Susan and said, "You must hold him."

Susan leaned back. "No thank you." The women and their intense eye shadows stared at her. Susan added, "I don't want to drop him."

Umm Josef put baby Josef in Susan's arms. "You be good. Just relax."

Josef closed his eyes despite the loud music. Mariam said, "He likes you."

Nader grabbed Susan's camera from her bag and said, "Smile!" The camera flashed two times. Susan cradled Josef's head and brought him close to her body. She breathed in his baby powder smell and stroked his soft chubby legs. She had read about a scientific study where grieving primates clung to their infants for days after they died. She imagined herself cradling Josef throughout the party, but then he began mouthing her right breast through her shirt.

Umm Josef and Nader laughed. Mariam clapped her hands and said, "He wants you to feed him!"

Even though it had been a month since Susan's breasts last leaked, maybe it could start again. Josef felt too heavy and his face looked too angelic. Her skin prickled, sweat broke out along her skin. She felt like throwing up and passing out.

She handed the baby to Umm Josef. "Please, I can't." Umm Josef glanced at Susan before joining another group of women, ones capable of properly fawning over a baby.

Mariam asked, "You have children?"

Susan patted her stomach, hesitating. On her first day of class at the seminary, Susan showed a picture of her husband and dog hiking in Moab, Utah. The seminarians asked how long she had been married, if she had children, and acted shocked when the answer was five years and no children. She said she was thirty and still had time, then joked that the dog was training, to see if they could handle a child. That was what she and her husband used to say before she became pregnant. One of the seminarians asked her why Westerners cared more about animals than people. At the end of class, another seminarian returned her pictures and said, "I will pray for your soul about your dog." Since that moment, she swore not to tell anyone about her baby, not even the other female teacher who seemed somewhat safe and friendly.

But Mariam, this pink-eye-shadowed woman, was eager and kind, and Susan might never see her again. Susan's husband and home seemed far away. Nader had left to take pictures of the dancing women with Susan's camera. Among the noise of the party, maybe Susan's secret could be freed, if only for a few minutes.

Susan leaned into Mariam and said, "I had a baby."

Mariam clapped her hands. "Wonderful! Do you have a picture?"

"He died."

Mariam made the sign of the cross and then grabbed Susan's hand. "May Allah bless his soul."

Susan blessed the language barrier. Mariam didn't follow up

with intrusive questions about how he died, how old he was. Just the one basic, unchangeable fact: he died. Maybe dead babies weren't unusual in Egypt. Susan hated that she found comfort in this.

Mariam stared at her and Susan feared that if Mariam looked long enough, she would find the truth. Susan added, "There's still time. *Insha'allah*, someday I might have other children." Although Susan didn't believe it, it seemed the right thing to say in this fertility-driven country.

"*Insha'allah*, I hope you have a girl and that she has your eyes and cheeks." Mariam pointed to Susan's sharp cheekbones. "She will be beautiful."

Susan's son had her stocky legs, or, as the doctor called them, soccer player legs. Susan had watched them moving around as her son kicked and waved to her and her husband. In that moment, Susan was reckless. She held her husband's hand and allowed herself to think of their baby with the name at the top of her husband's list: Lucas James. That was before their doctor noticed the missing part of his skull.

Asteer, the green-eye-shadowed sister, handed the guests plates with two pieces of cake—vanilla and chocolate. Sweets were rare in Egypt, so all special occasions were celebrated with sugary indulgences. Susan wished she had alcohol instead, difficult to find even in a Christian home. Mariam and Nader watched her. Susan ate a couple bites and then said, "*Lazeez!*" Arabic for 'delicious.' Frosting clung to the back of her throat.

The women began dancing again and Mariam grabbed Susan's hand. Susan shook her head. "Please don't. I'm not a good dancer."

Nader said, "You must. It's an insult if you don't dance."

Mariam led Susan to the dance circle, still grasping her hand. At the seminary, Susan couldn't touch the men, and they couldn't touch her, even though they could hold one another's hands, and

Susan liked being safe from contact. She had accepted the summer teaching position because she would be living in a building of celibate men, but she didn't foresee the parish children who liked to crawl on her and teach her Arabic. The seminary was a place for her to figure out whatever type of relationship she and her husband might still have. She avoided the morning Masses and during evening prayer she said the words, enunciating clearly for the seminarians, but spent the time wondering what her husband was doing. She hoped he was disassembling the baby room.

The women created a circle around Susan and Mariam, clapping and singing and shaking their hips, swirling around them. Asteer grabbed Susan's hips and guided them to the frantic beat. Nader held up her camera and instructed, "Say cheese!"

A big blocky man pounded into the middle of the circle, barefoot. Women bounced off his jolting hips like bumper cars. The women laughed and clapped, taking turns rebounding off his body. The rest of the men, including baby Josef's father, continued to sit in chairs along the wall. The block man's big toe twisted and turned against the floor as he shook his hips. Dark chest hair twirled out of his cotton shirt. He stomped his foot at Susan as if threatening to dance with her.

Susan turned to Nader, who stood on a chair with her camera. "Why don't you dance?" she asked.

"It wouldn't be right. I am not family." Nader explained Sebou parties were closed affairs, normally for family and close female friends.

"Then why are we here?"

Nader smiled. "A foreigner's visit is good luck. By being here, you bring that blessing into Josef's life. I am allowed to be here because of you."

Susan's son would have lived for one hour. That's what her doctor told her, and what her brother the doctor told her. The doctor and her brother had also said her chance of having another baby with the same defect was less than four percent. There was no known cause of anencephaly. Still, Susan suspected her husband's side. They may have deep blue eyes, but they couldn't be counted on for brain rims. She and her husband agreed an abortion was their only option, but Susan woke from dreams that sometime in the last four months of her fetus' growth God gave him a skullcap.

She told her brother she was thinking of keeping her baby. He said when he was in med school a resident discovered her fetus had anencephaly too. She carried the baby to term, against the doctor's advice. The baby died within an hour. Susan asked him how he knew, thinking this was a doctor's version of an urban legend. Her brother said a resident who helped deliver the baby was on her way to the morgue with the body but stopped at the second floor break room and asked the other residents and med students if they wanted to see an anencephalic baby. The dead baby lay on the counter swaddled on a blue surgery towel, the rough linen type, next to the coffee maker. The baby's body looked normal, but he was missing a brain rim and his oversized, frog-like eyes stared at the Sweet'N Low.

Susan imagined herself as that female resident, hiding with her dead baby in a room where no one could see him or study him. She would not have shared her baby for science's sake. She would have protected him from people who looked down on misshapen heads and frog-like eyes. She would have kept those last moments all to herself. Later, after her own baby was gone, Susan did some research and found the longest an anencephalic baby had lived was two and a half years, not an hour. When she told her husband, he said, "We couldn't afford a special needs baby anyway. That's not really living." And she knew then that her spreadsheet-making, always-prepared husband had discovered this research before the abortion and chose not to tell her.

The women stopped dancing and someone shut off the loud music. A chill ran through Susan, despite the hot room. Mariam and a few other women brought out blue candles with paper barriers to catch the wax. Women leaned their candles into the woman's next to them, spreading the fire. Mariam turned off the overhead light.

Nader told Susan, "They're going to make loud noises to scare off evil spirits."

"What are the candles for?"

"To bring light and God's protection into baby Josef's life."

The women began to ululate, that ancient sound that reminded Susan of Indians in old movies. Susan curled her tongue and joined in with that fast, turkey-like sound erupting from their throats. Some women banged pots and pans. They poured out of the apartment and then climbed down the stairs to the street. Outside, their candles burned and they shrieked with joy and terror and the thrill of making noise. The women entered the apartment building again and ran up the stairs, past the apartment, going higher and higher, until they entered the roof. They waved their candles, shrieked louder. The ones with the pans and pots stomped their feet.

The city of a thousand minarets spread before them. Sharp towers with crescent moons poked the sky. Some Arabic music boomed far away. To the right the Ramses train station shuttled people in and out of Cairo, carrying them into the surrounding deserts and far-away destinations.

Mariam grabbed Susan's candle-less hand and swayed with her, in time to the ululations. She said, "We protect Josef. His life, *insha'allah*, will know joy. Evil cannot find him."

Up on that rooftop in a section of Cairo where foreigners didn't venture, Susan and these women warded off the wickedness in the world, an entity more sinister than a jealous neighbor's evil eye, something worse than human frailty. Together, with their noises, their shrieks and their joys and their pain, they were a community united against the misfortunes that life can bestow. Baby Josef slept in his mother's arms, oblivious to any potential danger.

Mariam touched Susan's stomach. Susan almost dropped her candle, but hung onto it. Evil wouldn't find baby Josef because she couldn't hold onto a candle. Mariam bowed her head, made the sign of the cross, and then said, "*Insha'allah*, someday God will give you another child, a stronger one."

Susan imagined herself in that break room at her brother's hospital. Her husband was there and that dead baby without the brain rim was their Lucas James. Her husband would clasp their son's tiny foot within his palm, and marvel how it would disappear when he closed his hand. Susan would press their son's cheek next to hers, breathe in his smell, remember it, register it, so that she could call upon it and keep him with her. They would have known him, if only for a few minutes, and maybe that could have been enough.

Before leaving the party, Mariam kissed Susan's cheeks four times, a sign of great affection, and then gave her a plastic baby boy statue in a white net bag, surrounded with candy covered almonds, tied with a blue ribbon inscripted in Arabic with what Susan assumed was Josef's name and birth date. The little boy statue was a white, blond boy who held up a blue heart. "Made in China" was stamped in English on the bottom. If only her husband were here to appreciate the absurdity. She imagined the three of them in the Dead Sea—her husband, their Lucas James—not quite touching, but bobbing along, staying within each other's orbit. Susan gripped her plastic boy, bowed her head, and uttered, "*Mash'allah*," praying to the ceiling or God or whatever Egyptian deities that were still out there that her son was at peace, and that someday, *insha'allah*, he would forgive her.

Once I Lived Like a Stoop-Shouldered Idol

Michael Gaspeny

In second grade, I had to wear a corset, eyelets taut beneath my striped tee-shirts. Drifty, resistant to discipline, I couldn't bother to straighten my hunched shoulders. Fumble-fingered, slow to learn, lazy, too. My father burned as my humiliated mother tied my shoes before school. I walked across the steaming Norfolk blocks to James Monroe Elementary with my friend Arthur Ganiaris—a thin, tan boy who had nimble fingers and could tie his Keds. He saw my chafing discomfort. He led me under the porch of an apartment building into a dirt hollow, a shady den where stray dogs sometimes cooled off. Arthur freed the corset, which we hid under sycamore leaves.

The little cave faced Pinky's Tavern, where my Dad visited after work. Fetching him for dinner, I heard blasts of laughter from the shouting regulars. I had to stand outside and wait to be acknowledged, usually by one of the leggy women. I pointed and told Arthur, "My Dad drinks beer there." He smiled and nodded. His father ran the night grill at a bowling alley.

Each day after school, we slid under the porch, brushed the leaves off the corset, and Arthur laced me in again. Sometimes we went to his house, ruled by his dark, volcanic mother. She reminded me of the ear-splitting singers my parents watched on "The Voice of Firestone." Mrs. Ganiaris wore pearls and a blue tattoo on her wrist. In the dim dining room, the tattoo looked like columns over which the comic-book Superman soared during his around-the-world flights. Her shining necklace swung in the semi-dark over the table where her husband grumbled and smoked thin cigars called Between the Acts, packaged in a clinking silver and red tin. Once, staring at the ribs of the corset under my shirt, he said, "I want to ask you a question," but his wife gave him a sharp glance.

She wanted to put pudgy cheeks like mine on Arthur, so she stuffed us with baklava and little Greek cookies, shaped like statues, with tasty seeds. When she served us, I coveted her tattoo. It reminded me of the sticker in a Rice Krispies box, which my father had snatched from my fingers and thrown away.

One day, as Mrs. Ganiaris carried plates of honeyed delicacies, I said, imitating my mother's lilting tone when she complimented a friend, *That's a lovely tattoo!*

The dishes hovered over our heads instead of making their happy descent. I drooled and wanted to nudge her. Mr. Ganiaris snatched his cigarillo tin and left. After a long pause, pronouncing both words slowly, she said, *Thank you* and served the treats. She did not linger to enjoy our eating.

That summer, the Ganiaris family moved to Greece, homeland of Arthur's parents. I never saw them again. In Arthur's absence, my heart bulged beneath the scratchy corset. One night, I packed my comics in a cardboard box and ran away to the porch of his old building. A neighbor called my mother, who came with a deal: if I tried to stand up straight, she'd put the corset away. I surrendered, in my fashion. That fall, we moved to the suburbs, where I braced my shoulders, according to my mood.

Years later, at cocktail hour, when I was home from my listless studies at college, my father reminisced about Pinky's Tavern. I told him what a great friend Arthur had been, how he always knew the right thing to do. I didn't have to add that I was the opposite. Gazing into the past, my father popped a long-necked Budweiser with his prized battery-operated opener that boomed with a football announcer's gusto, *Ooo, yeah! Now for a beer!* For the first time ever, this voice offended him. Glaring at the opener, he told me Mrs. Ganiaris was a survivor of Auschwitz.

I saw the blue tattoo, heard my compliment from long ago, and blurted, *No!*

I told my father what I had said to her. I must have looked stricken. Over the years, I had exhausted his sympathy. However, on this occasion, he reached out, placed his hands on my shoulders, and said, *You couldn't have known. No one talked about those things then.*

His consolation touched me, but for the first time in my life, I rejected an easy escape. I didn't deserve exoneration. The Ganiarises had been good to me, better than I ever deserved. Arthur had patiently freed me from the corset day after day; Mrs. Ganiaris had spoiled and spared me. In my mindless innocence, I had not meant to mock her, but my compliment was self-serving. I had wanted a tattoo, and so I got one that night.

I found the fat Cuban cigar a fraternity brother had given me at his bachelor's party. I went to a lake near my house where I and a few other wastrels passed around jugs of Sly Fox as moonlight spread across the water and rose to us. I puffed up a good glowing coal, branded my wrist, and screamed as the skin crackled and popped.

My overall posture improved after that. The pink, scaly stamp on my wrist became my watch, the last gift from Mrs. Ganiaris's suffering.

First There Is a Mountain

David Hartshorne

The mountain west of our property rises 300 feet above the road to Madison. In Wisconsin it's called a moraine, grown from glaciers that backed off 20,000 years ago. It hasn't changed much—until four days ago anyway, when this downpour began. The last time it rained this hard was three years ago when Big Russ Bergen got electrocuted and it took twenty-five minutes for the fire department to shut off the electricity at the pole between Russ's bar and Pettit's Hardware just to get to the body. By the time my brother and I got there, three paramedics were pushing the stretcher through the slick back alley. I had to describe the whole thing to my brother because Harlan is blind.

The mortician, Mr. Daniels, always liked how quiet and respectful my brother was, so he let us visit Big Russ before he got started working on him. I wanted to stay, but Harlan didn't like the smell. I was hoping to see Jeanette, Big Russ's daughter. By then, I'd already asked her to marry me three times since we were kids. Well, four if you count that time I was drunk.

Harlan and I were leaving when Mr. Daniels shook our hands in the front parlor of the funeral home. "How you boys doing out there?" he asked. "Business good?"

"Yes sir," I said. "We got a supply of wood stacked for winter. More when this rain lets up."

"I'd like to get back to splitting," Harlan said.

Mr. Daniels pressed his lips together in a flat smile and shook his head while he looked at Harlan. "I don't know how you do it, son. How's a blind boy split wood?"

"Metal on metal," I said. "He could do it his whole life. As long as I held a nail steady, he could drive it home with any old rusty hammer. Isn't that right, Harlan?"

"Yeah, that's right." Harlan rubbed the top of his head. He always had trouble sitting quiet in a long rain. "I'd like to get back now," he said.

"Yeah, in a minute," I said. "Maybe it'll quit raining."

Mr. Daniels wrinkled his forehead. "And how's your mother these days, Augie?"

"Still got the cough," I said. "She's sure going to miss Big Russ."

It was Big Russ who made sure my mother stayed comfortable in the house we rented after our dad left, the same one Harlan and I live in now, out toward the moraine. He got extra help for us and kept after me to watch out for my little brother. Well, younger brother, because he's a lot bigger than me now.

You might've thought it was Easter all over again the way the whole town packed the Grace Lutheran at Big Russ's funeral. Harlan and I sat behind Jeanette, while her mother and mine cried dry tears at opposite ends of the front pew. Turning from one lady to the other, I almost couldn't tell which one was the widow. After the reception at Russ's bar, the Old Sauk, the storm started moving out. It was eating the ground four days straight, and when we got home I laid in bed watching the moraine shift beneath the lightning flickering off the clouds while Harlan and Mom talked in the kitchen. I heard Mom coughing soft and low. That was the last time I heard Harlan cry.

The rain stopped next morning, and I swear the moraine quit moving. We finally saw the sun again when Jeanette and I sat off the south bluff sharing a bottle of Southern Comfort. She told me what the whole town already knew.

"I don't care," I said.

"That doesn't matter to you? Your own mom?"

"I don't even remember my old man. He left when I was, like, three."

Her dad and my mom had been screwing around since before we were born and nobody else cared—why should I? But

38

with Harlan's high forehead and round nose, every year he got to looking less like my skinny old man and more like Big Russ.

"Does it matter to you?" I asked her.

"Enough to make me want to get the hell out of here," she said.

After finishing half the booze that afternoon, I asked her to marry me again and she stuttered as though she'd just met me, like she forgot all about when we were kids, tossing maple pods off the bridge and watching them spin down like helicopters, or playing pinochle instead of doing homework all through junior high. She left me by myself on the moraine that day, throwing sticks and pinecones against the back of the "World on Wheels" billboard. I swore the next time I asked her to marry me, I'd have a big diamond ring for her.

Russ's wife, Mrs. Bergen, left town for good not more than two weeks after the funeral. She found out he'd left the Old Sauk to Jeanette, and he left the rental house to us. We didn't care she was gone—she kept all to herself anyway. Whenever we did see her in town, we could hardly breathe from the lilac perfume percolating from her sweater.

Jeanette never got along with her mom—worse that winter she was sixteen and Mrs. Bergen swung a belt buckle at the side of her head. Got Jeanette knocked out and bleeding so bad she had to go to Minnesota for a week to recuperate. I left a message every day until she came home and kept homework notes for her in school. Then I got to joking about how she must have smarted off one too many times. Harlan didn't laugh at my joke, rubbing the top of his head and sulking in his room whenever he got mad. I reminded him how it was me who got him the job on the football team.

That was the summer we were buying light bulbs at Pettit's Hardware with our mom when the high school coach, Jack Billberg, stopped us. He wanted Harlan to try out for the team, even though Harlan couldn't see. He could clog the middle, Coach said. Mom didn't like the idea.

"Oh, Harlan's not a regular fifteen-year-old, Jack, you know that. If it weren't for Mr. Bergen, he wouldn't even be in school. You got a good mind though, don't you, Harlan? No, I'm not letting him get hit upside the head every Friday night."

"Well, how about Thor, Mom?" I said. "Coach, aren't the Maulers looking for a new mascot?"

Harlan flexed his arm. "I could be Thor," he said.

When the season started, Harlan paced the sidelines wearing a blonde wig and swinging a maul they commandeered from the hardware store.

Now my brother is even stronger. He swings an eight-pound sledge like it's a sixteen-ounce claw hammer. He never misses that wedge. It's like the sledgehammer and the steel wedge are magnetic and Harlan always swings true. Whenever he's out splitting wood, I can feel the strokes working their way inside our house, vibrating through the loose boards on the low porch. The crack on metal pulses like electricity up my legs and into my arms, all the way to the palms of my hands. Even in a heavy rain, Harlan splits cordwood until he can hardly lift the hammer, splitting and stacking, and filling up every empty space. I figure it's how he keeps from crying, handling a hammer for his grief. Maybe he's filling the space our mom left when she died six months ago.

Ever since this rain began, over these past four days, the moraine looks like it's traveled a half-acre toward our pump house. Harlan shuffles in and sits in front of the hearth, a pile of mustard sprigs between us. We separate the seed just like our Grandma Cora did, rubbing our hands back and forth over chipped ceramic bowls to liberate the seed from the pod. I hold my favorite blue pot and Harlan cradles a wide yellow bowl, his favorite, between his thighs. He reaches for dry twigs from the pile and runs his palms together, blowing the chaff straight toward the heat of the fire where he listens for the spark in the heat of the flame. The reflection on his face makes his eyes look like brand new dimes.

"You miss her?" he says.

"Sure," I say.

"Everybody dies," he says.

"Well, duh," I say, and I'm stupid for saying it. "Look, Mom's better off now. She was in a lot of hurt."

"I know," Harlan says.

"When this rain stops, we'll go to the cemetery," I say.

He gets up and walks into the kitchen and I hear him tapping a fistful of coriander into his pot. I'm still rubbing my pods together when he tells me we're low on vinegar.

"I'll go out tomorrow," I say. "Maybe I'll stop at the Sauk and see Nettie," and it's then I hear the ceramic bowl hit the kitchen floor and Harlan swearing under his breath. Every time, I'm thinking. This happens every time. I can't say a dang thing about Jeanette. I can't say anything without him rubbing his head or dropping something.

Before I flip on the light, I can feel the vinegar soaking through my socks and the coriander like birdshot on the bottom of my feet. Then I see Harlan's yellow pot split on the floor in three big shards. "What happened—forget where the counter is?" I throw a dishrag at him and spread his fingers apart, just to be sure. "You're not bleeding," I say. We wipe the floor on our hands and knees, quiet except for vinegar sloshing and the rain spitting against the window.

"Her name's Jeanette," he says. "She doesn't go by that other name anymore. Not since school."

"What's a matter with you? I've always called her that. Look, I'm going to The Sauk and I don't care. And until I get that alternator fixed, I'm walking."

Then we stand up and he's looking straight over my forehead, his eyes twitching, and he's working his mouth, too, but he doesn't say anything. Instead, he turns around and fills the sink for the mop. I drop the broken bowl in the trash and ball my socks up in the towels and push the wet pile across the counter before I snap off the light and head back to the rocking chair to put my bare feet up in front of the fire. Twisting a sprig of mustard between my fingers, I watch small drops leaking from the roof, spattering on the warm hearth before they hiss and disappear.

Before breakfast I open Harlan's bedroom door. "I'm running into town. Need anything?"

"Some of that grain bread. And Mountain Dew," he says.

"Why don't you come on with me? Nothing going on here."

"I got splitting to do." He turns on the bed and pulls the blanket over his shoulder.

"It's raining," I say.

"I know it's raining."

I tug the sheet down to cover his soft feet. "I'd like you to come along today, Harlan."

"What for?"

"I got something I'm gonna do."

He pulls the blanket again and talks into his pillow. "You just want me to carry shit," he says.

"Not that," I say. "It's a surprise."

"I got splitting to do."

"Jesus, suit yourself," I say, and shake my head. In my room, I pull the little cardboard box out of my underwear drawer and look inside it one more time. Mom didn't wear this diamond for twenty years or more. I grab my rain slicker and stash the ring in the side pocket.

By the time I get to the Old Sauk, the light coming through the clouds makes the building glow orange, like a fire in the cellar. I slog up the front steps onto the wide porch, water pooling where the wind bends the rain in. When I open the heavy door, I see half dozen people sipping drinks, listening to the Bracker Sisters' "Ain't I Winsome?" on the old jukebox. Jeanette doesn't look up from behind the bar.

"Boots," she says.

"That's your song, Nettie," I say. I'm rubbing my boots on the big mat and fumble the little box out of my slicker. Nobody notices, but now she's looking at me.

"Where's your brother?"

"Metal on metal," I say and sit at the bar. "I'll take a Berghoff."

When she took over the family business, Jeanette stocked up on good beer. The antique cash register still sits in front of the big mirror but all the beer posters are gone. Now she's got framed prints of wooden ships on tall waves, splashing up against white sails mixed in with big rainclouds. There's a picture of an old castle with some sheep on a green hill, and next to the ladies' room she hung a night scene of the Eiffel Tower.

I'm running the cardboard box between my fingers and stick it in my top pocket before taking a swig of beer. Jeanette is staring at me in the mirror, then she steps out to wipe a table near the big west window. She's working a towel around the napkin tray when I walk over and point toward my house.

"Get a load of the haze off those clouds, Nettie," I say. "Our moraine looks like it's sneaking into town."

She stops wiping the table and looks out. I smell menthol on her breath, and I feel the tiny hairs of her arms on the back of my wrist. I see the pores on her nose and specks of black mascara in the wrinkles under her eyes.

"Sooner the better," she says and slaps the rag on her palm. "You better go see about Harlan." Then she turns back toward the bar.

"Hold on. Wait a second, Jeanette. Tell me something. Why are you still all concerned about Harlan? Look, I know he's your brother, too—half anyway—but he's a big boy. He gets along fine. He wants to stand out in the rain, that's his business."

"You like it. You let him."

"Like it? C'mon, Jeanette, he's got energy to burn. It's better than getting eaten alive in this crummy little town. What else is he supposed to do?"

"He's blind, Augie, he's not stupid."

"That's right, he's not stupid. If he wants to get wet, he gets wet. He's got a choice."

"Choice? What's he supposed to do—stand on the sideline wearing a stupid wig so people can laugh at him?"

"He hasn't done that for years. And nobody's laughing at him. He was part of a team. You know what that's like Jeanette—a team?"

Rick Leiber clears his throat. "Harlan made a good mascot."

"Shut up, Rick," she says and stops behind the bar. "Listen, Augie, you think you're doing great, don't you? You got a real team there, don't you?"

"A blind boy used to been stuck in a group home," says Paw Peterson.

"That's right, Paw," I say. "That's right, Nettie. We *are* a team. We're a family. You and me and Harlan. Where would he be without the Maulers or Big Russ? Everybody looks out for Harlan. Where would he be without us?"

"Oh, give me a break," she says. "Where in the hell can he go? That moraine has moved farther than you have in twenty years. Nothing's changed. None of you. And Harlan's the one who's penned in."

There are six other people in the bar and everybody's looking into their drinks. She turns her back and faces the mirror. The old cash register clacks quietly when she runs the rag between the rows of loose keys. I stare at her reflection through glass shelves. She rubs the front of the coin box, and except for the rain slapping outside, the whole place is quiet until somebody's ice cube cracks in a cocktail glass. She keeps on wiping and shakes her head. "It looks like lightning out there, Augie. Just go."

Then the overhead lights flicker and something rumbles in the cellar. Paw looks at Jeanette between the bill of his Maulers cap and his vodka cocktail and speaks first. "That's just thunder, you know."

His wife, Irene, wears blue jeans and a pink sweatshirt under a Maulers jacket, her gray hair gathered in a loose bun. "You kids make up, now," she says.

"Wait a second, Nettie," I say and nod toward the kitchen. I press the cardboard box inside my pocket as I push through the door. She takes her time following me in. Then I hold my palms up, waiting for her to speak her mind.

She shakes her head, but she won't look at me. She tightens her arms across her chest. She looks at the floor. "The rain. This rain."

"What?"

She starts in about rain that never stops. Three years ago her dad dies—a storm like this. Then before that, when we were sixteen. "Remember that storm?" she says. "Just like this one. Pouring four days straight and the goddamn Maulers still played."

She tells me how she ran into the warming house at the game that Friday night. "It's the only place I could get a smoke," she tells me.

Harlan was in there, rubbing his head, nervous. Everybody else sat in the stands, toughing it out. Jeanette just wanted a smoke and forced Harlan to take a drag of her Newport. She was making him laugh, teasing him—leading him on.

"Yeah, so?" I say. "Harlan got teased a lot. Not your fault."

"Well, I didn't know anything," she says. "I didn't know shit, Augie. I was sixteen. My mother was already over the edge, but I didn't—I didn't connect anything—I didn't think. When she found out about me and Harlan, she completely lost it."

My voice echoes like I'm standing in the empty cellar. "What, you? And Harlan?"

"That's why my dad took me to Minneapolis," she says. "It wasn't just Mom and the goddamn belt. And it wasn't Harlan's fault. Just me. It was me. I never thought it through. Dad made Harlan swear never to say anything. And you can't say anything either, Augie, about knowing anything. Especially to Harlan. I mean it."

I reach for the spigot on the steel sink and the cold water

45

streams through my fingers. Outside, the rain spits like birdshot across the windows, and I push the backs of my hands hard against my throat. When I step into the bar, everybody's staring into their drinks. I toss my damp rain slicker over my back and walk out.

On the porch I touch my pocket, the little box against my chest. The mud on my boots puddles on the boards before washing between the cracks in the pouring rain. I hear the strike of metal on metal, steady strokes running through my shoulders like electric shocks pulsing to the palms of my hands. Beyond the trees the moraine has shifted again, a quarter mile this way, moving right toward my house.

Hawaiian Odyssey

Henri Bensussen

Georgjean squinted through binoculars and studied her bird guide, back and forth, till she felt nauseous. Was that dumpy bird poking the muddy creek bottom a short-billed Dowitcher or the more common long-billed one? The creek passed under a bridge and flowed in a wide arc to the ocean. A man and woman pushing a baby buggy approached and stopped at the bridge. The woman took a plastic bag from the buggy and threw handfuls of popcorn into the water. Three Mallards swam close and lunged at the white treats as if bobbing for apples on Halloween.

She glared at the couple; didn't they know the rule against feeding wildlife? The woman responded with a carefree smile that signaled *Wanna fight?*, and threw another handful into the water. The ducks quacked for more. No signs of life emanated from the buggy. Was there even a baby in there?

At this point in the story, her writing group pounced on the contentious subject of Point of View. Charles said, "It's incorrect to allow the woman feeding the ducks her own POV."

"Why the need for only the narrator's POV?" Georgjean tried not to sound impatient.

Charles furrowed his brow as though preparing it for a planting of corn. "Keeping to one POV shows the writer knows the rules, has technical expertise."

"So it's a matter of politically correct behavior? No one else gets to talk?" She looked around the table, but the others kept their eyes focused on the pages of her story.

"Georgjean is telling the story," Charles said, "and she can only tell us what she sees or thinks. The woman's POV, the *Wanna fight*, has to be surmised; she can't blurt it out." His lips parted in an ingratiating half-grin. "That goes for the quacking ducks, too. We can't know if they want more popcorn, or if they're simply giving thanks, or no thanks."

Maryann said, "The ducks could be commenting on something else altogether."

"I hope this isn't something we have to vote on," Michael said, "because I'd have to abstain." Michael disliked dissension. Georgjean found his critiques dull and without insight.

"Anyone for tea?" Maryann pushed back her chair. The others nodded, glad to sidestep the question of author style versus rules of proper writing.

Maryann put water on to boil, and Georgjean, in the lull, escaped back to the creek and the problem of identifying Dowitchers. Assuming the objective third-person, she accepted the risk and wrote in her notebook, *L.B. Dow east of bridge, Sunday, Oct. 17, 9:15 a.m.*

Turning her back on the hungry Dowitcher and the shameless Mallards, she walked onto the beach. A fresh set of odd, large footprints paralleled the ocean. Georgjean figured them to be male, and she wondered about his Point of View, if he were conscious of one. Many people never noticed anything but breaking waves, or acted out of a very personal POV, like that couple with their baby-less buggy of popcorn.

White-bellied Black Turnstones and dowdy Surfbirds scurried about on the offshore rocks blending into the scenery so well they looked like rocks themselves. A sudden breeze ruffled her graying, curly hair. Glancing toward the dunes, she saw a hut knocked together out of driftwood. In the open doorway a man waved. She waved back. His gaze drew her closer and closer across the sand until she began to suffocate in a strange, thick atmosphere of unwanted intimacy. He wore only a paisley-patterned loincloth. A dark blue arabesque of beard swirled across his face and golden yellow eyes held her in a hypnotic gaze. "I've been wanting to meet you," he said.

If a lizard could talk, it would sound like his voice, Georgjean thought. He extended a pale scallop of a hand. Georgjean tried to fend off his touch but was overcome by a shroud of ice. The ice melted her skin into a pool at her feet, where a ball of mist enveloped it. Her skin glowed faintly inside, like a spent light bulb, as the ball bounced into the hut.

"Sit with me a moment." He patted a blanket woven of seaweed. "It's slimy, yes, but comfortable for those with sensitivities."

Shivering, she saw that his skin was rather leathery and dry compared to hers, or what she remembered of it. "Look, mister, whoever you are, I want my skin back. I'm cold."

"I have a story to tell that will warm your heart, and if you listen, I'll return everything I've taken from you."

Georgjean wondered what else was missing from her person. Stripped as she was of outward definition, she had no choice but to make the best of her situation. Folding her arms, and noting her biceps showed unexpectedly good muscle tone, she said, "I'm sorry, in this format only one Point of View is allowed, so I'll have to tell your story for you, after you impart it to me away from anyone else's hearing or eyesight."

"Look, the beach is empty, it's just you and me, and I'm going to tell my story." He grasped Georgjean's bony wrist. "Sit still and listen."

He was rather handsome, in an exotic way, and she did want her skin back. Though it had become wrinkled, thin, and scarred, she was used to it.

"I like your skin," he said, as if reading her mind.

"Thanks, but if you're thinking of a trade, forget it. Get on with your story before I come down with pneumonia." She sat beside him and closed her eyes.

"Once upon a time," he began.

"Cliché," she said.

"It was …"

"No drama in an opening like that. Start with an action, or some dialogue."

"It's my story."

"It's our story, and if we want it read, we have to follow the rules of writing." She snuggled closer. "Give it a proper start or I'm out of here, skin or no skin."

He grumbled, cleared his throat, and looked up at the sky, which had turned a gasping shade of green. "Once, long ago, I met my true love, Myrna, but she left me, and now I search for her, across the Argentine pampas, through ice and snow atop the Arctic circle, and here on a beach in California." He remained silent for some minutes.

Georgjean sat up. "Is that it?"

"Not enough?"

"Plot requires action—you've launched an arrow but it hasn't hit a target."

"Ah, right. Here's some more." He uncrossed and re-crossed his legs, assuming the full lotus position. "Thoughts of Myrna haunt me night and day, her oiled locks of black hair cunningly arranged, her leopard-spotted arms, and eyes like those of a blue parrot. She fascinates me and I'm determined to hunt her down. When I catch her, I'll keep her in a jewel-encrusted cage with velvet covered bars."

"You're so full of yourself," Georgjean said. "And that's a tired plot line. Spurned lover tracks down his goddess, and thinks she'll fall for an offer of treasure and a life of luxury in a velvet cage. Considering her attributes, your Myrna is probably making her own millions as a rap star or performance artist."

"It's the only story I have." He turned his back and his shoulders shook with sobs.

"Enough with the sentiment. I'm ready to go home. Where's my skin?" Near the doorway, Georgjean spied what looked like a pair of long johns hanging on a peg. She jumped up and pulled it on, one leg at a time. Immediately she felt warmer, more contained. "What's your name?" She flexed her fingers; her brown eyes blinked relief for the return of lids.

He sniffled. "John."

"Everyone's named John. Couldn't you come up with something more literary, with a subtle reference to a famous novel or author?"

"I've been traveling and haven't slept in weeks. It's the only name I can think of."

Georgjean patted his back. "I've tried to make you a sympathetic character, but it's not working. I'm afraid this is goodbye."

"You're leaving? How heartless you are. I feel like I'm being put in a coffin and buried."

"Sorry, my darling, but that's your problem." With a wave of her hand, Georgjean marched off across the sand clutching her binoculars. Were those small birds with black legs Sandpipers or Sanderlings? She couldn't concentrate and felt uneasy about the escape from Barefoot John. Had she been too harsh? She glanced back at the dunes like Lot's wife checking to see if God really would be nervy enough to destroy Sodom. Was God even interested in her or her bird-watching, and what about the pillar of salt—why did God choose that as punishment, what was His point?

Eyes pinged at her consciousness like cherry pits. A herd of nervous California Gulls circled as if they were children listening to a ghost story around a campfire that reflected its flames in their horrified eyes. She focused the binoculars for a last, daring look at the spot where Barefoot John had waved to her. A tin can hanging from a twisted piece of driftwood glinted in the sun and the sky melted from green to blue. She trudged back toward the bridge. The gulls parted to let her pass. She licked her dry lips and tasted salt. Overhead, a raven soared low and loudly snorked. Georgjean thought it very like what Myrna would say if she had anything to say about it.

Maryann broke in on this reverie. "I'd like to learn more about Myrna," she said. "The raven could link us back to the dowitcher."

Michael said, "You're asking a minor character to highjack a perfectly respectable tale of religious insight." He shuffled through the pages of Georgjean's story. "Here on page six is the problem." He pointed to the third paragraph. "This business of the gulls, describing them as a herd. Is that correct?"

"You're always picking on these minor uses of word choice, Michael," Charles said. He grinned, and Georgjean realized there were certain traits of his that she disliked.

She was quietly pleased when Maryann said, "Au contraire, Charles. Word choice is at the heart of good writing. Cows herd, but birds flock. Let's recognize the difference and honor it."

"My real point," Michael continued, "concerns the change of scene to gulls and a raven when a more satisfying ending would be the commentary on God." He looked around the table. "Too radical? I only meant it as a deft way to reach resolution." Coughs and sighs greeted his explanation. "It is about how a lonely person turns to religion for solace, isn't it?"

"Maryann is right," Charles said, ignoring Michael. "I, too, want to hear more about Myrna. It would be more plausible and interesting to end the story with her."

"I didn't mean to rewrite the story," Maryann said. "Let's break for a moment. Tea's ready."

Georgjean slumped in her chair. She hadn't been writing about a lonely person searching for God. She'd merely followed some mindless meanderings into the realm of the right brain's archives. Up there an attic full of dusty clauses and worn-out troubles held memories stored willy-nilly in undarned socks nibbled on by mice, who ended up with ulcers and died. Not a place to linger.

She stared out Maryann's dining room window, poking a finger into the curls that escaped from the headband she always wore and trying to ignore the conversation around the table. A bright sun blinded her. Her bare feet sank into wet sand. Gulls flew in a white-gray cloud, squealing like a pack of pigs. A raven croaked. "I have a story to tell," it said in a cacophonous voice.

"And what do you have to add to this narrative?" Georgjean said. "I'm ready to toss it."

"I'd like to have my side heard." The raven settled at Georgjean's feet. "I'm Myrna."

"I should have known. Oiled black hair, or feathers, but not the eye of a blue parrot, though you do have a bit of a moustache."

"My moustache gives me an edge that some find intimidating. Useful that way." Myrna stroked the hairs above her beak with her left wing, exposing leopard-like tattooed spots.

"It's hard to put the two of you together—you and John. How was it for you?"

"Strangely beautiful if you enjoy sex with a lizard. It became boring. He's a one-position guy, and you know how that is."

Georgjean felt a bond of sympathy with Myrna and also with men, so many of whom were stuck in childhood habits. "So you abandoned him, leaving him rebuffed and lost."

"Too demanding—you got a dose of that, didn't you?" Myrna took a moment to groom her tail feathers. "I split for L.A. to take in the art scene. When that got old—too much yogurt, not enough potato chips—I flew to Cabo for some rejuvenation; great fish tacos in Cabo. Now I'm back, but not for long." Myrna gave a little hop, crooked her sleek head, and stared up at Georgjean with a sharp eye outlined in kohl.

"He misses you. Couldn't you check in with him before you leave for your next vacation?"

"He'll find someone new. He always does. Believe me. We've had many rounds of this plot line. But, hey, what about your situation?"

"Mine?" Georgjean stepped back as if slapped.

"These writers with their fixation on points of view. It's time you and I got to know each other better, and where better to do that than Honolulu?" The raven named Myrna leapt into the air and circled above Georgjean. "You'll find me at the Bongo Club on Waikiki Beach, excellent pineapple kabobs." Waving a wing, Myrna caught a thermal and disappeared.

"Georgjean, are you with us?" Michael snapped his fingers in front of her eyes. "I suspect she's over-identified with her character," said Maryann.

"She seems to be asleep."

"I wonder if it was the tea. I tried a new kind, Hawaiian Odyssey."

Charles drained his cup. "It's so strong we could easily be carried away ourselves. I've always wanted to see Hawaii."

Maryann gazed into Charles's eyes, ignoring Michael. "While Georgjean is bird watching we steal away on Myrna's thermal and have a glorious evening at the Bongo Club . . ."

Michael stood with a jerk and knocked over his cup. Muttering about a lack of compassion, he strode into the kitchen looking for a towel to wipe up the tea. Returning, he found the others gone, the house silent. He stood at the open window and noticed a long, black feather on the sill. What if, he wondered, Georgjean had put them all under a spell with her outlandish story?

Georgjean's ability to step outside their writerly community of credos and precepts always astonished him. He stared out at the view, beyond the poppies and straggly lavender, the overgrown vestiges of a vegetable garden, the broken down back fence. He missed her, he realized. Out there was the ocean, above it an afternoon sky, and a breeze that foretold afternoon fog. Had Georgjean based her story of Barefoot John on him? He felt his heart beating right through the skin, cotton, polyester, and lamb's wool that covered it safely and well. His wife was waiting at home. They were to meet friends for dinner.

It was the tea, that was obvious. He studied the box. *Hawaiian Odyssey.* A long list of suspicious ingredients. He picked up his satchel, strode out the front door, carefully closing it, and unlocked his car. He was not the kind of man, he reminded himself, who fell for fantasy writings about lizards and popcorn. Nor women who couldn't keep their hair under control, letting it curl around their ears and hang over their impossibly dark eyes as they made their silly jokes.

Area 52

Roger Hart

I'm driving Rocky's car, a state-of-the-art hybrid SUV with more gizmos, buttons, and dials on the dash than the cockpit of a stealth bomber. I have no idea what most of them do, and I'm afraid to touch a knob or dial for fear I'll get ejected through the roof or send a distress signal to the Pentagon. Rocky doesn't want his car sitting idle while he's in Antarctica studying dark matter with Sloane, my housemate, friend, my question mark. He's trying to sell the car to me.

Then things got complicated.

"We need a little more air back here," she says.

I look at the switches, dials, buttons, and knobs. Oscar leans forward, his hand poised momentarily in front of the panel and touches a screen. Oscar's pushing seventy.

"Thanks," Sloane says. "That's better."

But it's not. Sloane's in the back seat with Rocky. What is she thinking? She told Oscar to sit up front because of his long legs. I don't like the arrangement. Everyone along for the ride to welcome my father home is a terrible idea. Sloane took the call from Larry, my brother, and he asked her to come, and she said I was working with Oscar, and she'd pass the message, and he said for Oscar to come, too. My brother loves to have an audience, the bigger the better. "The more the merrier," he said.

So here we are, cruising down Route 7 along the Ohio River. I don't feel merrier, and I don't understand why Rocky was included or why he agreed to come despite his insistence I test drive his car. He doesn't know my father. He doesn't know why my father was in prison unless Sloane told him, which she swore she'd never share. Maybe I'll tell Rocky jealousy and violence run in my family.

I'm taking the long way to my brother's, an hour drive along the Ohio River, which is more scenic than the forty-minute drive on the freeway. The scenic route is my excuse, the reason I've given everyone in the car for the longer drive. It makes me sound like a good guy, which I'm not. The real reason is I want to postpone our arrival as long as possible.

"What do you think, Rocky?" I ask, nodding toward the river. I'm trying to hide my anger that Rocky came along.

"About what?"

I glance in the rearview mirror. Rocky is looking at Sloane, not the river. At least I think he's looking at Sloane. Rocky's eyes don't point like they should. "The river," I say. "The Ohio River."

"Ah yes, very pretty."

Sloane and Oscar have met my mother and brother, so they know what they're getting into. Rocky has not. None of them have met my father, whom I've seen during brief visits to the prison where we sat at a cafeteria table, where he sometimes sobbed, not over killing the woman but how he missed driving his old Pontiac.

I thought Sloane and Rocky might talk science, cosmic rays, dark matter, maybe the false vacuum problem, all mysteries of the universe. But no. They swap university gossip. Who did this, who said that, what about the new dean, and was the secretary fired or did she quit? Oh, and the budget cuts. How many faculty positions will be eliminated?

"How about dark matter?" I say to the backseat. Dark matter, what it is and finding it, is Rocky's thing.

"What about it?" Sloane asks. Dark matter and powerful cosmic rays are her thing.

I don't know what about it. That's why I asked. Invisible stuff that makes up most of the matter in the universe and no one knows what it is. How is that possible?

Rocky leans forward, grips the back of my seat. "We have a number of experiments going that may give us answers." He and Sloane mumble back and forth.

"A few physicists don't think it exists, but Rocky will find it," Sloane says.

Oscar gives me a sly smile. He's dressed in bellbottom jeans and a blue button-up shirt two sizes too big for him although the baggy sleeves enhance his bald, old hippie, gaunt look.

My brother lives in a secluded area near the Hocking Hills surrounded by trees and large rock outcroppings. This being a Sunday he will have spent the morning preaching and praying.

I try to prepare everyone for the visit. I explain that when my brother prays before a meal the food is cold by the time he finishes. Rocky, the Muslim, laughs. Oscar, the Buddhist, laughs. Sloane, the lapsed Catholic shushes me, says I should be kind. I don't practice any religion, which may be why I'm unkind, thinking things like Rocky should take a swim across the river. I warn them: "My family is strange."

"We're all a little strange," Oscar says. He starts humming a song by The Doors.

A barge pushes coal up the river.

I lived in the Hocking Hills during my last year of high school and loved the ledges and wooded hills. Deer and wildflowers, mushrooms in the spring. Old Man's Cave, Rock House, Conkle's Hollow. In the fall, the whisper of the wind in the trees and the crunch of leaves beneath my feet. My brother was never happy there. He never walked into the forest or climbed one of the rocky slopes. But here he is, living at the edge of the park in a house that looks like a Yellowstone lodge. The gate at the end of his drive is open, and gravel pops beneath the tires as we pass through shadows of red pine.

I pull a deep Zen breath, park between my brother's big-as-a-bus camper and the First Church of Hope and Salvation van.

Oscar takes it all in, the house, the three-car garage, the massive stone chimney, the manicured lawn, the piles of food on the picnic table, the flowers along the front of the house. "You say he's a preacher?" he whispers.

I nod. "A televangelist. Has his own television and radio show."

"Think it's too late for me to become a televangelist?

"You're a Buddhist," I say.

Oscar runs a hand over his bald head. "Maybe I could be both."

My brother steps out the front door followed by Ruth, my sister-in-law, and my mother. He hugs Sloane, who introduces him to Rocky who gets a two-hand handshake. "Oscar, my good man," he says, wrapping an arm around Oscar's shoulder and appearing genuinely happy to see him. "Freak!" he whispers to me. And then to everyone, "Let's go. We're late."

Been here thirty seconds and I'm already puzzled. "Late for what?" I don't see my father. I look at the food on the picnic table. I'm hungry.

"Pick up Dad," he says, jangling keys in his hand. He points at the church van. "All aboard!"

"I thought we were meeting him here."

"No, no. We're picking him up at the gate. Come on. We're running late."

Larry holds the door of the van open and again tells everyone how happy he is they could come.

The van has barely enough room for Sloane, Rocky, Oscar, my brother, my mother, Ruth, their four kids, and me. "We can wait here," I offer. It's a selfish offer. I don't want to ride in the van with Larry driving. The high center of gravity makes these vans dangerous, and my brother drives like he's aiming the Olympic luge down the chute, leaning this way and that while hoping to make the next curve. Besides, someone should guard the food.

"No, no. Dad wants to see everyone at the gate," he says as he swings behind the wheel.

Helium-filled balloons float against the roof of the van. I want to point out that there's only so much helium on the Earth, rather in it, and no more can be made. Once it's released in a cheap balloon it's gone, goodbye forever. Liquid helium super cools super magnets in MRI machines. It's used in the production of semiconductor chips and is needed for scientific research. Before I can speak up, my brother slams the door shut and we're off. Sloane's in a seat wedged between my mother and Rocky. Oscar and I sit behind them. If I was wearing a tie, I could loop it over Rocky's neck and strangle him.

We are in a church van on the way to pick up my recently paroled father from prison while my brother tries to lead us in a campfire church song I don't know, but he and my mother insist I do. The song, he says, is how we'll greet my father.

If I were my father, I'd ask to stay in prison.

The singing quickly peters out, and Larry gives us a running monologue about the area, which I only catch bits and pieces of, while he takes curves and hills too fast. The van leans hard to the left, then hard to the right.

He says, "We're running a little late."

My father has been in prison for eighteen years. Ten more minutes will not matter.

The curves come fast and hard. I feel claustrophobic, too warm. The collar of my t-shirt presses against my throat. My stomach goes down when we go up a hill and up when we go down. I try to focus out the front windshield, but the view is obscured by balloons and heads. We go too fast over a hill and for a few seconds my stomach floats behind. I know where the prison is, and I know how to get there, but Larry is taking a different route. I can't tell where we are or how far we have to go. I need air.

"Freak?" Oscar whispers.

"Later," I say.

He leans closer. "You okay?"

I can't look at him. I can't turn my head. I have to concentrate.

"You don't look so good," he says.

I try to focus straight ahead. "Open the window," I say.

Oscar wrestles with the window latch without success. "Won't open," he says.

The van is too warm. I can sense Sloane and Rocky turning in their seats, looking at me. Larry takes another curve too fast, another hill where my stomach does a flip. Coffee and a cream cheese bagel churn in my chest. I burp and taste last night's hotdogs.

My head feels like it's been detached from my body. My stomach gurgles in protest. "Stop!" I yell.

Larry doesn't stop.

Sloane leans forward in her seat. "Stop the van! Russ is sick."

Larry whips the van to the side of the road and slams on the brakes, throwing us forward in our seats. I open the door and fall out before we come to a full stop. I land on the ground, stumble, and step away from the van.

Larry watches, waits for me to throw up.

"I'll stay with him," Oscar says.

"It's your driving," Ruth says. "You're taking these hills like a maniac."

"He always got sick in the car," my mother adds.

Larry holds up his hands, maybe pleading with the Lord, maybe explaining to the occupants of the van. "Just trying to get there when Dad's released. We wouldn't be late if Russ had gotten here on time."

Sloane passes a water bottle to Rocky who leans out the door and hands it to Oscar. "Hey," my brother calls out. "Relax in the shade. We'll pick you up on our way back."

The door to the van slams shut and they're off.

"You okay?" Oscar asks.

I'm embarrassed. "The breeze feels good," I say. Thirty-two years old and I get motion sickness like a three-year old. I hate this sign of weakness in front of Rocky. What the hell was my brother thinking, driving like a fool over these hills?

"I wasn't feeling so good either," Oscar says.

I look around, try to get my bearings. I'm not familiar with the road. We're surrounded by a forest, and there's a large boulder with a flat top perfectly situated in the shade. When we sit on it the coolness seeps through my jeans.

"Getting your color back," Oscar says.

I'm feeling better although I'm not ready to get back in the van.

Oscar holds out the bottle of water. "Drink?"

We pass the bottle back and forth. A breeze rustles the leaves. Crows, high in the tree across the road, scold us. "And you?" I ask. "How are you? I mean, how are you really?"

He doesn't answer right away. It's like he's taking inventory of how he is.

"From gung-ho marine to peace-loving hippie to old bald guy," he says. "It happened fast."

"You're still a peace-loving hippie," I say.

He nods. "You've got that right. And a marine."

As if a gunnery sergeant gave us the command to stand, we both get to our feet and walk down the hill. I'm not wearing a watch, so I don't know how long the freedom van has been gone, but it should be coming back this way soon. "Sorry for dragging you into this," I say.

"No, no," Oscar says. "It's been entertaining."

We stop at an old forest road that cuts into the hill and disappears in an overgrowth of trees and lush fern. It looks inviting.

"Better not," Oscar says, reading my mind. "Might miss the van."

A cop car comes down the hill, shoots past us. The brake lights come on as it goes around the curve. A few seconds later the car appears again, going much slower. I get a bad feeling, a flash premonition. Dark clouds, thunder, and lightning.

"What'd you do now?" Oscar asks.

My first fear is Larry's flipped the van, and someone told the cops we were out here waiting. My second thought, upon seeing the casual way the cop climbs out of the cruiser, is that we're about to be harassed.

"Fellas," the cop says.

The voice is familiar. I can't identify it, but I get a sinking feeling we're in trouble.

He's wearing dark shades that hide most of his face and walking with an exaggerated stride, maybe from the weight of the gun, handcuffs, radio, pepper spray, flashlight, taser, baton, and bullet proof vest. He's working gum or a wad of tobacco. One hand rests on his belt, ready to draw. He could have stepped straight out of *Smokey and the Bandit*.

"Russ?" he says.

I hesitate, not sure I want to admit I'm me. "Yes?"

He steps closer. "I'll be damned. It's you. Don't recognize me, do you?"

"Your voice," I say. "Your voice is familiar but ..."

He takes off the sunglasses. I see his face but it's his name tag that seals the deal. Charlie Palm. Last time I saw Charlie was when he punched me in the jaw fourteen years ago at a high school party. "Charlie!" I say, trying to sound as friendly as possible. He has a gun.

"Russ!" He opens his arm and gives me a man hug. "Wow," he says, stepping back but still gripping my shoulders.

I'm at a loss for words, so I point to Oscar. "My friend, Oscar," I say. "And this is Charlie Palm." I don't know what else to add. *An old high school friend?* Not even close. *A bully who made my life miserable?* True, but not wise. He has a gun.

"I was the high school troublemaker, got into all kinds of trouble," Charlie says, finishing my thoughts. "Russ was the science guy."

Oscar shakes Charlie's hand and since the gun has not been drawn and the cuffs are still on his belt I began to relax. A little.

Charlie spits out his gum, a wad the size of Denmark. It lands an inch from my shoe. "Can't believe it's you. I gotta tell you, this is weird."

"It is," I say.

"No, I mean seeing you here, next to the trailhead. This

place is like Area 51, you know, the place where the UFOs landed out west. This place might be even more special. I call it Area 52. It gives me goosebumps." He holds out his tattooed arm to show me the goosebumps, but I don't see any. The tat is a shark mating with a mermaid.

He changes the topic, asks what we're doing on the road, no car. He asks how I've been, if I'm married. He holds up his hand, shows us a wedding band. "Eight years," he says. "Have two boys."

We go back and forth with small talk, how we're waiting for my brother to pick us up and how long Charlie's been with the force, and then he returns to the goosebumps and how he can't believe he saw me here, at this trailhead of all places. He tilts his head in the direction of the old logging road. "Only person I've told about what happened up here is Amy, and I'm not sure she believes me. But you were into science and I trust you."

Sloane would question the idea that I'm a man of science. Oscar and I work maintenance at the university. Why Charlie would trust me is a puzzle.

"Back there," he says, pointing up the trail, "'bout a mile in. I was camping. My twenty-first birthday. I was planning something crazy that could've gotten me in a heap of trouble. I won't say what, but it was big." He stops, laughs like this crazy thing is still a possibility. "I was up late, poking the campfire, working out the fine details of my plan when the rocks began to glow. I shit you not. I'd had a bit to drink and thought the heat from the fire was responsible. I touched a few stones, and they were cool."

He stops, looks at Oscar. "You won't breathe a word of this, right?"

Oscar makes the motion of zipping his lips.

"Yeah, okay. Well, more rocks began glowing, marking a path deeper into the woods. You know, like in the Handle and Grateful fairy tale with the cake crumbs. Maybe I was curious or in a trance. I followed the trail until I came to a small clearing where this beam of blinding blue light shot down out of nowhere. I couldn't move. I swear, one minute I'm standing in the woods and the next I'm sitting in a special chair with a doohickey thing clamped on my head."

Charlie stops again, studies our faces to see if we believe him. Oscar and I respond with sincere looks, eyes wide open, a little slack-jawed, as if we're about to say, *Wow!*

Satisfied, Charlie continues.

"It was them." He gives a sly nod toward the sky as if the aliens even now are watching, ready to snatch him away again. "They never hurt me, but there was a funny odor in the air, like electrical wires burning. I woke up back at my camp, in my sleeping bag twenty-four hours later. Afterward, I had no desire to do this deed I'd been planning. I went a hundred and sixty degrees the other way. And here I am."

I don't know what to say. He has a gun.

The cruiser radio squawks. A female dispatcher requesting something for a 10-16.

"Sorry," Charlie says, as he spins around and runs to the cruiser. "See you."

Seconds later, the siren is on and he's racing up the hill.

Oscar and I exchange a look. "Glowing rocks." Oscar says.

"Doohickey thing clamped on his head," I answer.

"Handle and Grateful," Oscar says.

Oscar and I wait. I don't know what's taking Larry so long. Maybe they've changed their mind about releasing my father. I'm annoyed with my brother and embarrassed to keep Oscar out here waiting. What was Larry thinking, driving these roads like a maniac? And Sloane! She's off with Rocky to greet my father as he gets out of prison while I stand beside a road in the middle of Area 52.

Oscar and I walk up the hill to the spot where we were dropped off. Walking feels good. The cool boulder where we were sitting is in the sun and warm to the touch. We're about to climb the embankment and wait in the shade when the van appears, slows as it approaches and then stops.

The door opens. Everyone is laughing and talking, enjoying ice cream cones. The helium balloons are gone. My father is driving! He doesn't have a driver's license, hasn't driven for eighteen years! He's all bones and angles. His chin, brow ridge, and hooked nose give him a hard edge. If he was a Rorschach test, your answer would be knife. "Hey, Dad," I call out.

"Russ," he says. He pats the steering wheel.

Oscar swings the door shut and we start down the road.

"Sorry for keeping you waiting," Larry says. "There was a long line at Dairy Queen."

Sloane leans over the seat, holds up the last of her vanilla cone. "I would've got you one," she says, "but I was afraid it would melt by the time we got back to you. Here, want the rest of mine?"

I shake my head although a chocolate cone would taste good.

"You'll never believe who we just saw," I say.

"Charlie Palm," Larry says. "We saw his cruiser fly by. Fine man. Found God. Goes to our church. He's one of our deacons."

I want to say he found aliens, too. I don't. Larry having guessed who we saw I decide to try again. "And the other night Oscar and I were at the ballgame in Cleveland and guess who we saw there."

Larry begins naming the starting lineup.

"No, no. Well, yes, we saw them, but I also saw Cass. Remember Cass?"

Ruth touches Larry's arm and shakes her head.

"Cass? Cass your imaginary girlfriend?"

Everyone leans forward in their seat, wanting to hear the story, even the kids. Despite my father's nearly two-decade break from driving, he's keeping the van on the road although our speed fluctuates between too fast and too slow. "It's these brakes," he says.

What?" I ask. But before Larry continues his story, I know what this is about. He never met Cass the summer she lived with her grandparents across the street. He was away at camp.

Then, when I ran into her again years later, he was off at seminary school. Every time I mentioned her, he called her my pretend girlfriend and said she was a figment of my imagination and desires.

"She wasn't, isn't, imaginary," I say.

Distracted by the argument between his two sons, my father momentarily loses control of the van, and the tires hook the edge of the road, throwing us to the side before he quickly corrects and throws us the opposite way.

"Does he still talk about his imaginary girlfriend, Sloane?" Larry asks.

Sloane looks at me and grins like she's not sure.

"Larry." Ruth says, a soft warning.

"It was embarrassing," Larry says. "This imaginary girlfriend—her name was Cass?—continued all the way into high school and college."

I want to remind my brother about what happened between Cain and Abel, and if he keeps up this shit history will repeat itself. "Mom," I say. "You met her, the girl across the street when I was in seventh grade? Dad?" I've resorted to asking my parents to stick up for me in this stupid argument with my brother. Pathetic.

"Sorry, honey," she says.

My father's concentrating on the road, tapping the brake too hard as we enter every curve.

I can't let this go, not yet. "I saw her at the ballgame Friday night. She was sitting behind the bullpen."

Everyone looks at Larry and then at me, waiting to see where the story goes, but my father catches the edge of the road again, and we all fall silent, hoping to survive the next curve.

Larry prays as we sit around two over-sized picnic tables loaded with food, which, including the potato salad, has been sitting in the sun for over two hours. "Bless this meal," he says. I figure I'll believe in the power of his prayer if no one gets food poisoning.

He continues to pray, and after a few minutes my mind wanders and my eyes open. Rocky's on the other side of the table across from Sloane. I catch him wink at her. They both quickly bow their heads and pretend it never happened. My brother continues to pray, thanking the Lord for each person present. "Thank you, Lord, for bringing my father home, so we can be together again. Thank you, Lord, for my mother, who …"

A tom turkey emerges from the trees and slowly walks toward the drive, its beard almost touching the ground. A breeze ruffles the paper plates. I want a slice of the cake, which I saw on the kitchen table when I went inside to use the bathroom. Chocolate. Three layers at least.

"Thank you, Lord, for my brother, and please take away the sickness that plagued him earlier as we …"

The tom struts as he stares at his reflection in the door of Larry's silver Lexus. He holds his wings in a display of dominance, turns sideways, and comes back to the hubcap again and again, strutting, threatening the tom he thinks he sees, torn between the real and the imagined.

I do a lot of thinking as Larry prays. After I have a slice of that chocolate cake, I want to return to Area 52, hike up the trail, build a campfire and wait for the rocks leading off into the woods to glow. I'll follow that glimmering path as far as it takes me, and, when the brilliant light comes out of the sky and aliens whisk me up into their ship, I'll beg them to take me home, wherever it is I came from. I'll bet Cass will be there.

Thinking's Deadly

Heather Mateus Sappenfield

The trail curved through aspens torched by autumn. Leah paused, tilting her face to the sun, letting it needle her flesh. Behind her closed eyes, she saw Galen hurtle past that frozen waterfall. His red harness, cinched across his parka and pants, trailed slack purple ropes. His metal-clawed boots kicked the air, and the wind rolled his hair around his helmet's edge. Nearing the frosty boulders, he looked at her. But she turned away, just as she had that day. She'd not thought to cover her ears.

It was midmorning, the busiest time in the coffee shop that she now owned alone. The Wired Bear was the hotspot for locals and tourists, famous for the bantering between its fearless athlete owners, and for Leah's guffaw. A patchwork of photos from magazines like *Powder, Rock and Ice,* and *Rapid* papered the walls. Many of the pages were autographed by their friends. Some featured Galen or Leah. It was the perfect business because afternoons, they'd closed shop and played hard. Friends ran the place now, had been running it for close to a year.

After the shock wore off, Leah's parents, even her kid brother, had asked, "How could he be so irresponsible?" But Leah didn't regret Galen's choice that day. Or any day. The hazards of the ice when he ascended, the rapids when he kayaked, the chutes when he skied were what made Galen alive, and Leah had loved him alive. She'd adored his hair askew, his smile wide with his crooked front tooth bumping his lip, and his eyes leaking adrenaline, had loved that fate-tempting countenance from the first moment they'd met.

They'd been kayaking in May's snowmelt, had vied for the

same standing wave, paddled to a shoal to have words, and fallen headlong in love.

He'd always been a little better than her at every sport, and this had pissed Leah off. He'd see her frustration and say, "You're better looking and you've got more skill, but thinking's deadly." Leah would swell with fury for hours, till she'd burst into a guffaw, because he was right: when she took these risks, she needed to trust her body. Leah had adored Galen so much, she'd not minded when she'd drifted into his shadow. She'd even stood in it as he'd fallen, but then it had drawn tight beneath him, and there'd been that doughy thud.

What Leah regretted was that Galen had left behind so little of himself. Nothing but clothes, photos, a kayak, five pairs of skis, and two bikes. He'd given her no jewelry, only gear, and, for the first time, she understood jewelry's true allure as an emblem one could wear after the one who had gifted it was gone. Her wedding band was just a tattoo around her finger. After five years of marriage, when she was thirty-two, she'd started mentioning children. "We have all the time in the world," he'd say. Did he realize his mistake as he fell? Did he think, There will be nothing left of me but gear?

Leah clung to this trail behind their home. They'd hiked it together countless times, and its cliffs, meadows, and creek had been their sanctum. She moved along it now, her body latched to a narcotic sense of him.

She smoothed back hair that had escaped her braid. Tonight she'd numbly open a can of soup, or crack spaghetti over a steaming pot, and stir it as the TV droned on. Friends would drop by. "You never laugh anymore," they'd say. "When will you start kayaking again? Or climbing? Or skiing? Come to the Wired Bear tomorrow."

"Soon," she'd lie.

Cupping her face in her hands, she sensed if she could just cry, she'd be freed from this margin. She hadn't cried at the accident when their friends had said, "Ah, God! Ah, God! Don't look, Leah!" *They'd* dialed 911. Rescue workers had carried away his broken body.

Steps scuffed from down the trail. Leah moved into yellowed wheatgrass and scarlet-tinged Oregon grape, pretending to scan the cliffs, hoping this wasn't someone she knew. The hiker passed, she turned, and the spread of his shoulders, the narrowness of his hips, the muscling in his calves, the gentle curl at the ends of his hair—stop!

Yet the way he moved.

Leah reminded herself of Galen's memorial, held atop the ski mountain, three hundred people gathered to acknowledge his death. She'd stared into the middle distance, dry-eyed, arms rigid at her sides.

She started up the trail, telling herself she was headed there anyway. Her heart quickened because in the hiker's stride, in the swing of his arms, *was* Galen. Her eyes blurred, and then he was Galen. She moved faster, got close enough to touch his back. He glanced over his shoulder, and he was not Galen.

Leah shuffled to a rock and plopped down, mashing her eyes with her fists. A squirrel darted to a pine, scampered up, and chattered at her. Ahead, the trail bisected an avalanche chute strewn with boulders and wild rose, and the hiker disappeared around a bend.

She squinted at the trees and the frost-singed asters, an addict scrabbling for reality. She inhaled moist dirt heated in the sun. To the blue above she said, "Take me with you, Galen, if that's what you want, but I can't go on like this!"

After a week Leah returned to the trail. The sky was laden with snow clouds, but the air was warm. She paused to appreciate a stand of glowing aspens that would not endure the coming storm. Their beauty would vanish, stored in their roots. Looking down, she wriggled her toes.

Leah ran. The rocks and ruts required quick precise steps,

so she didn't gaze down the curves or into the alcoves of trees, rather focused on navigation. She reveled in the long absent airiness of her strides, sensing this was healing.

She topped a rise and didn't see the bear. A northern breeze clacked through the leaves, carrying her scent in the other direction, drowning out her steps, so the bear didn't notice Leah either. Trying to stop, she reached forward, and her fingers disappeared in fur. The bear wheeled, bounced twice on its front legs, and lunged. She felt the pads of its paws on her shoulders as she landed against a wide rock. Its claws pierced her chest. So this is how it happens, she thought. She saw her ghostly reflection in the beast's beady eyes.

They regarded one another for seconds, an eternity. The bear snorted, its head snapping down, its weight compressing her chest like resuscitation. It hopped off, hustled to the side, and studied her. Finally, it snorted again and sauntered away, glancing over its shoulder three times.

Leah lay immobile, watching, the backs of her fingers flattening cool grass, her palm still feeling fur. She inhaled against the pain in her chest and noticed a feral scent that she realized was hers. Eyeing the low clouds, she barked one bleak laugh.

Leah awoke in bed, vividly sensing the bear looming over her. Her skin was slick with sweat and she tasted fear. Each night since the encounter, her dream of Galen falling had been replaced with her own apparition in the bear's eyes.

She drug herself up, peeked through the curtain, and discovered snow falling gently in the predawn light. At her dresser she pulled out clothes to go slog through her soreness on the bike path. Each day she'd forced herself to run, determined, but failing, to recapture that sense of healing she'd felt on the trail.

Leah leaned toward her dresser's mirror to bump her fingers along the punctures on her chest. They curved up from her shoulders to her clavicle, then down, meeting in a dip over her heart where the inside claws had been. At first, they'd been scab jewels in a bloom of purple, red, and yellow. When the bruises had begun to fade and the scabs fell away, they'd revealed exquisite burgundy indentations. This scar necklace seemed a covenant. Of what, she did not know.

The night the last scab disappeared, Leah woke in its stillest hour and ambled, naked, to the chilly garage. They'd always parked their truck outside because the garage was stuffed with gear. Now the kayaks, skis, bikes, snowshoes, and ice climbing equipment seemed to taunt her.

She approached Galen's kayak, leaning in its rack. Tracing the tiny bumps of its rough plastic, she conjured the stubble of his cheeks. She caressed each gouge made by the rocks he'd defied, the rolls he'd survived. Studying her tattooed wedding band, her craving for him spread to every pore. She imagined herself paddling into this spring's churning runoff, maybe where they'd met, saw herself stab the water with her paddle and roll under wearing no helmet, her hair swirling in the current. She'd paddle, inverted, so she'd never come up. Hugging his kayak, she pressed her cheek to it, but sensed only its sharp plastic smell. Her embrace deteriorated to clawing, and then her fingers pulled into fists. She punched the kayak, three jabs that scraped her knuckles, so she pummeled it with the sides of her fists, her blows sounding like drums. The kayak fell to the floor, rocking high along its side, then it whunked onto its bottom. Leah kicked it, not caring that her toes screamed, but it skidded only a few feet across the concrete.

She gathered as much ice climbing gear as would fit into her arms, the cold metal pressing against her breasts. She fumbled with the lid of the bear-proof trashcan, then dropped it in. I should sell this. This is wasteful, she thought, yet she hefted all Galen's gear to the trash.

Her snowshoes hung on the wall beside the can. She lifted them down and brought them inside for the morning.

One person had tracked out the trail, and over those footprints lay two inches of fresh white. Vegetation lumped and poked through in reds, greens, and yellows. Leah tugged her hat low over her ears and relaxed into a jog, steps wide to accommodate her snowshoes. She scanned the trunks of aspens and the shadowed pines for movement.

As she approached the place where a month ago she'd met the bear, she slowed to a walk. She brushed off the stone she'd landed against and studied it, matching the sore places in her back to its shape. Leah imagined the scene, bringing her hand to her coat, tracing her necklace of scars, feeling each memorized bump. She whispered, "Sweet dreams," to the hibernating bear.

Leah resumed jogging. She passed the bend where she'd seen the hiker who'd resembled Galen and continued to the spot where she'd let him go. The same squirrel chattered at her from the same tree. Looking up at it, she said, "Keep my secret. You're the only one who knows I'm crazy." The word "crazy" seemed to float before her and she swatted at it. She remembered how good it had felt to punch Galen's kayak, to throw away his gear, but even in death, he was right: it was time to trust her body.

She ran down, each step cushioned and sliding in the way she loved. Just as she abandoned herself to it, she discerned bear tracks crossing the trail. Veiled by new snow, she'd missed them on her way up. They led in the direction her bear had gone when it had sauntered away. Searching a sky so blue it made her squint, she flexed her fingers, feeling her knuckles' violence against Galen's kayak. She stepped into the bear's tracks.

Her snowshoes sank awkwardly in the prints, making her work to maintain balance. She followed them through a stand of spruce and down a gentle slope to an icy creek. Peering along its gurgling course, she spied two downfallen logs, and navigated toward them through bowed sedges. The logs were narrow, but Leah inched her snowshoes along them to the watercress-lined bank.

From here the bear's tracks were purposeful and straight, climbing the valley's north wall. Their path curved around a majestic spruce, ascended to a ledge against a cliff, and disappeared into a cave. Breaths heavy from the ascent and limbs numb with apprehension, Leah forced back her doubts.

On the ledge she gazed out across the valley, could make out one bend in her trail, and realized this bear had probably watched her and Galen hike, had known them together. On all fours at the cave's low mouth, she peered in. I wish I knew more about bears, she thought and, they'll never find my body, then, Don't think! and she crawled through.

The bear's scent made her cover her nose. Kneeling, she waited for her eyes to adjust and eventually discerned a fur crescent against the far wall. The hair tracing her spine stood on end, and she retreated toward the bright hole behind her. But she stopped, forcing herself to witness the rise and fall of the creature's ribs, to hear its torpid breaths. The cave was almost warm. She pulled off her gloves and inched closer, lifting her toes to keep her snowshoes from scraping. Reaching out, she brushed her fingers over the tips of its fur. She inched daringly close and lightly rested her palm on its flank, thrilled by her audacity.

Galen would be stunned, she thought as her hand rose on each inhalation. Even he wouldn't have the guts for this. Beneath the fur was living heat, the first she'd felt since Galen. A buzzing surged through her, and he appeared before her, falling. Yet she also felt the wind of his descent against her own face, felt her legs kick wildly, saw the boulder-strewn ground approaching. And then she saw herself clearly, standing rigid, watching, her eyes locked on her own lifeless gaze. Her vision reeled back within herself, and she watched Galen land with that mortal thud that concussed her chest.

Her breath rushed out in a burning cough. Gulping down

panic and guilt for not wanting to die, she retreated frantically out of the cave. On the cliff, she straightened, dizzy and blinded by sun and snow and what had just occurred. Fighting a sob, she stumbled and her snowshoe screeched.

A grunt seeped from the cave. Another. And the sound of motion. Leah heard a bark like a surprised dog, and the rasp of claws.

Leah ran, her snowshoes clanking as she lunged around the spruce and cut the distance to her escape by leaping off the cliff. She sailed, arms windmilling, and landed, tumbling once. She lunged up, sprinting.

She heard the bear's huffs and the whoosh of its paws through the snow as it gained on her. Her foot stopped cold, and hinging face-first into the snow, she knew the bear's paw pressed the back of her shoe. Twisting to face its attack, she screamed, more animal than human, "Enough!"

They were within an intimate boundary.

The bear stepped back. It grunted, and then its mouth hung open, black lips flared to reveal fangs. Leah thrust out her palm, commanding, "Enough!" She brought her hand to her chest. "You know me. You gave me jewelry."

The bear lowered its head and swung it, side to side. It stepped from foot to foot as if dancing. Leah thrust out her palm again, and the bear plopped onto its rear. It dropped its head low but forward. Leah tittered.

Drawing her foot firmly beneath her, she forced herself erect. She brushed off her torso and realized she was bawling. "Thank you," she said. Though she longed to touch the flare of fur below the beast's ear, she turned to her tracks, grief streaking her cheeks, and did not glance back.

Three strides took her across the logs spanning the creek. She climbed the rise through the spruce and ran down again.

The trail seemed changed, now simply tinged by loss. The sun cast her shadow before her. Her tears thickened in the cold, blurring her vision. As she rubbed her eyes, her toe caught on a root and she sailed, landing before she could get her arms out. She bounced hard on her chest, plowing snow, two leaves, and a rock with her face until she careened to a stop. It hurt like hell, and she had a bloody nose, yet she was alive. Alive! Leah rolled, gasping, onto her back, and guffawed.

The Lavender House

Jen Knox

The dead arrive on a diagonal plane. They whisper inconvenient truths. For this reason, or maybe to mess with me, they visit when I'm brushing my teeth or mid-conversation. They speak loudest when I'm somewhere between consciousness and sleep, when my guard is down.

My daughter, Diane, is no different. She arrived for the first time on the anniversary of her corporeal death. She told me to expect a visitor, and I immediately knew who it was. I barely got to say goodbye before her spirit flitted off, but that night I dreamed of pressing my palms into a willow oak's bark until I became the tree, rooting into the earth. I woke up with a delicious feeling, a connection so deep that it can't be anything but sovereign. It faded when I looked around my room.

The Lavender House, a "mental health facility for the elderly," provided us single-serve coffee pots after we exhibited good behavior for six months. I had one of the smallest rooms, so I had to keep mine on the floor. I sat next to it and examined my appearance in a handheld mirror, trying to ignore the peeling wallpaper in the background. As my single-serve coffee brewed on the linoleum, I pulled three goddess cards and wrote an affirmation on the mirror in erasable marker. I wasn't allowed to light candles, so I imagined the full ritual.

I was still in my nightclothes when a nurse I'd never seen arrived and glanced at my affirmation, which was illegible to anyone but me. She kindly insisted on shoving pills down my throat, like the rest of them. I successfully slid the small, pink ovals to the top right quadrant of my gums as I drank the full paper cup of water. This nurse wore all white with polka-dot socks, but her energy was red. Her blood pressure was high. I stared at a mole on her forearm as she took my vitals.

"I don't like you," I said.

"What did I do ... Amelia?" she stammered, double-checking her chart.

I sized her up, answering with a shrug. This woman was a maker. She would be happier if she started selling crocheted purses or monogrammed mugs. She wasn't a caretaker; she was destined to create things that people could use with mild entertainment. It would make her joyful. This work would kill her.

"You really don't like me?" she asked. Her body was deflated, exhausted.

I took a breath and spoke from my diaphragm so my voice wouldn't shake, and said, "I don't like the pills. I don't like the garish walls in here. I don't like much about this place, and you're a part of it." When she nodded as though she understood, I pedaled back. "I think you should find new work. Old crazies like myself know things."

"I don't understand," she said, circling AGGRESSIVE on my daily summary sheet. I saw a scale for paranoia and hygiene as well. My diagnosis was schizophrenia, which is what the doctors labeled anyone they didn't understand. Years earlier, the word was mania. Before that, hysteria.

Softening my tone, I said, "You know, my granddaughter will be visiting me soon. She's a really special girl."

"That's ... good. How old is she?" she asked with a half-smile as she glanced at my fingernails, then my hair. She circled ACCEPTABLE under hygiene.

"Almost an adult," I told her. She didn't register my answer at all. Her finger traced the checklist as she looked in my closet and under my bed, then stuck out her hand.

"My name is Doreen. Have a lovely day, Amelia."

I smiled, waiting for the quietest moment before I unleashed a guttural scream from the top of my lungs. The shaking that came from avoiding pills for four days straight made it more intense, so I pushed the sound hard from my chest. I filled the room, the halls. It was a bit much, I know, but I was bored. And I wanted what was best for Doreen. She had to quit before she became complacent. The look on her face told me I'd done my work.

I got along with few residents at The Lavender House, but most were not long for this world. The ones who would hang on for as long as I would were mean because they knew, on a cellular level, that they had a longer sentence.

When 8 a.m. arrived, after a brief visit from the doctor, I journeyed to the cafeteria for a bagel. I rarely ate in there. It was so sterile and full of bustling workers and sad residents. Sometimes excitement came in the form of thrown condiments or hair pulling, but it was mostly depressing.

The library and fireplace were nice areas to sit alone or with the quiet ones. The pond could be serene, and few people were there when the geese weren't patrolling it for scraps. After wrapping a bagel in a paper towel, I searched for my friends.

There were two residents I most enjoyed spending time with. They were named Gloria and Glory—a similarity they'd bonded over as soon as they met. Glory was senile. Gloria was obsessive-compulsive with trauma-induced paranoia. They were mild cases, all in all, and I was their entertainment.

Gloria had been a flight attendant. Glory had been a career waitress and mom eight times over. They said next to nothing when we played cards because they were both so wildly competitive in a Midwestern, passive-aggressive manner. They knew to defer to me when selecting movies on Sundays because I had a knack for picking the perfect one for the mood. In reality, I just chose films with handsome men. Glory's face completely changed when I played anything starring George Clooney.

Ours was a transactional relationship. I knew they'd sneak me their cookies or Danish to appease my sweet tooth, and they knew I'd keep them entertained. One day, they even asked me to pull cards for them, and I enjoyed their nervous delight as I shielded the bad news with mystery and exaggerated the good news.

I took a seat by the fireplace with my warm bagel and tore off a piece as I opened my notebook. Writing was the best way to pass time here—to delve into correspondence with the future or past. That morning, I didn't even hear the walker as they approached.

"Are you writing a short story? Can I read it?" Gloria asked. It was a letter to Jake, a man I would see again soon, but I didn't share this information. She said it read like a novel. Perhaps this was her exaggeration, but it made me smile.

"Amelia, you should have been a writer. Read this, Glory."

More prone to jealousy, Glory nodded hesitantly, then asked if we'd like to play Hearts. I told them I had another idea. "Follow me," I said. We walked past the pond without looking back. I led them beyond the paths and welcome signs. When we entered the woods, I could feel the shift in the electromagnetic field.

You'd think we were in elementary school the way those two giggled as we took a step past the property line. We journeyed into the woods surrounding us and got lost in birdsong. Still in her slippers, Gloria was slowest, and I continuously had to shush her when she yelped at the mud on her pants or the sensation of a stick brushing her ankle.

We saw a rabbit and two deer as we found the opening of a narrow trail. Of course, Glory scared them away when her walker hit a rock. We moved, albeit slowly, as far as we could. I was bending over to unlace my shoes when the rush of fast-moving feet arrived. We turned to find five staff members there, so serious in their head-to-toe white, and I began to laugh as I shoved my palms into the earth.

Doreen, the new nurse, quickly attended to Gloria, so she wouldn't have to be the one to walk me back. She made her decision to quit at once: I could see it in the way her pupils contracted for an extended amount of time. I took the opportunity to look around for the tree I'd dreamed of and thought I saw one in the distance. As we were led back, I tried to ask, but the staff was huffy.

Upon our return, they locked the doors for the evening, and called my son-in-law. I was in trouble, like a small child, and I sat in the library, waiting, as the "incident" was recorded. Jenny, the spunky young woman who sat at the front desk and would no doubt be at The Lavender House until she too was a resident, told me that while I was off gallivanting, my granddaughter had called multiple times.

"I told her that you were indisposed. Amelia, you must stop getting in trouble. I know you and love you, but some of these workers think you're better suited for the east wing."

"What's the difference?" I asked.

"I wouldn't see you, and I'd miss you." She paused. "You look a little pale. Would you like some blush?"

I let her adorn my face with the cheap makeup she sold to all the nurses. The angle of the brush conjured memories of my mother's severe cheekbones. I told Jenny a fictional story about an old crone who found the secret to youth, only to realize that being a crone was far more rewarding, and at the end she clapped. Checking her computer, where notes about "incidents" were reported each day, she told me I was now scheduled to eat lunch at 11:30 instead of 12:30, to give Gloria and Glory their space. "According to what Doreen wrote here in your file, the two Gs said you were the ringleader." Just like that, I'd lost my friends.

"Jenny, tell me, are there willow oak trees in that forest?"

"There are all kinds of trees back there."

"Helpful. Thanks," I said, catching sight of my wrinkled coral-colored cheeks.

That night, I wiped the message from my hand mirror. "We are only constrained by ideas." As I waited for a corporeal visitor, I wondered who would visit my dreams. I hoped my daughter again, maybe a messenger I had yet to meet. But instead, there was silence. The night arrived, and I stared out at the distant forest feeling proud. The day had been satisfying.

Jason Who Will Be Famous

Dorothy Allison

Jason is going to be famous, and the best part is that he knows he will be good at it.

He has this real clear picture of himself, of him being interviewed—not of the place or even when it happens, but of the event itself. What he sees is him and the interviewer, a recording so clear and close up, he can see the reflections sparking off his own pupils. It's hi-def or Blu-ray or something past all that, a rendering that catches the way the soft hairs just forward of his earlobe lift and shine in the light reflecting off his pale cheeks. All he has to do is close his eyes and it begins to play, crisp and crackling with energy as the microphone bumps hollowly against the button on his open collar.

"A lot of it, I can't tell you," he says, and the interviewer nods.

Jason is sitting leaning forward. His features gleam in the bright light, his expression is carefully composed, focused on the interviewer. Jason nods his head and his hair swings down over his forehead. One auburn strand just brushes across the edges of his eyebrows. The interviewer is so close their elbows are almost touching. He is an older man with gray in his hair and an expression of watchful readiness—a man Jason has seen do this kind of thing on the news before, someone to be trusted, someone serious.

That is the word. Serious. The word echoes along Jason's nervous system. He is being taken seriously. Every time he imagines it again, the thought makes him take a deep breath. A little heat flares in his neck as the camera follows his eyes. He looks away from the interviewer, and his face goes still. He looks back and his eyes go dark and sad.

"I'm sorry to have to ask you about something so painful," the interviewer says to him.

"It's all right," Jason says. "I understand." He keeps his expression a mirror of the other man's, careful and composed. He can do this. Piece of cake.

Behind the cameraman, there are other people waiting to speak to Jason, others are standing close by to hear what he has to say. Everyone has questions, questions about what happened, of course, about the kidnapping and all the months in captivity. But they also want to ask him what he thinks about other things, about people, and events. In the interview as Jason sees it, he always has answers—surprising and complicated, wonderful answers.

"That boy is extraordinary," he hears the serious man tell another.

Extraordinary. The heat in his neck moves down into his chest, circles his diaphragm, and filters out to his arms and legs. He hopes it does not show on his face. Better to remain pale and impassive, pretend he does not hear what they say about him. How extraordinary he is, that everyone says so, some kind of genius. He half-smiles and then recomposes his expression. Genius. Jason is not sure what his genius is exactly, but he trusts it. He knows it will be revealed at the right time, in the right circumstances. It is simply that those events have not happened as of yet. But they will.

He opens his eyes. He has stopped at the edge of the road. Dust, whitegrey and alkaline, has drifted up from his boots, and he can taste eucalyptus and piney resin. He looks up the road toward the next hill and the curve down into the shade of the redwood stand there. Should have brought a bottle of water, he thinks. Then, extraordinary. How would you know if you were extraordinary? Or a genius? He's pretty good at math, and music—though nothing that special. If he worked more, put more of himself into the work, no telling what he might not do. His dad told him that, once, when he was still living with them.

His teachers have said something of the same thing. All of them though, his dad, teachers and his mom, they say it like it's a bad thing—his talents and his waste of them.

"If you worked more. If you worked harder."

They don't understand. No one does.

Jason wipes dust off his mouth and rocks his head from side to side. He knows the problem. It's not that he's lazy or stupid or even scared. No. The problem is that he never has had enough time or focus. There's just always so much that has to be done, and how does anyone do that kind of kung fu stuff anyway? How does anyone become extraordinary? Like Uma Thurman in the Tarantino movie? Years going up and down staircases. It's like that. You do some stupid thing over and over and over, and sometime along in there, you discover you have achieved this enormous talent.

He glares up the road and resumes his pace, boots kicking dust and his hands gripping the straps of his backpack. He could do extraordinary stuff. Given the right circumstances, he has everything in him to do stuff that will startle everyone. It just takes the right circumstances— getting everything out of the way. He nods to himself. He can feel that coming toward him—the opportunity, the time, and the focus.

He has dreamed it so often, he knows it is coming—though he doesn't know all of how it will happen. That too, he sees like a movie, the movie of his life going on all the time. Step in and it is already in motion. Like that. He grins and speeds up slightly. Might be, he will be walking home along the river road from Connie's on a day just like this one. He'll have something in his backpack, after working for Connie all day, doing what he does so well, little baby buds his specialty. Connie always tells him how good he is. He knows exactly how to clip and trim and harvest only what is ready to come away, leave what should be left behind. That shows talent. That shows aptitude. Bonsai killer weed work, he does that all the time. Connie knows she can trust him. Some people she strings along, but him she always pays with a ready smile and a touch along his arm or one quick knuckle push at his hip. Cash or buds, she pays him, and that's all good. Just as it is good no one knows what Jason has in his backpack. No one knows his business.

Still, he knows, the day is coming. Someone is going to snatch him up right off the road or outside the liquor store downtown—some old guy maybe, or even one of them scary old dykes from out the bay side of the Jenner beach. Those bitches are dangerous and he can barely imagine what they would do with a piece of work like him. Everyone knows they all got stuff, guns and money and stuff. Bitches like that stick together. But maybe it will be someone from nowhere nearby, some bunch of crazies with some plan he will never fully understand, that no one will understand.

He nods slowly, his hands gripping the straps tight as he imagines it—the snatch, the basement, the months alone and everything that comes after. He has been seeing it for a long time, the story in his head, the way it will happen. It was a dream the first time, a nightmare, grabby hands and the skin scraped off his knees—a nightmare of sweaty basement walls and dirt in his mouth. But by the third or fourth time he dreamed it, everything receded and it was not so nightmarish. He was fighting back and able to think. Then it was magical how he started thinking about it in the daytime, daydreaming it, planning what he would do, how he would handle things. Then what came after the snatch became more and more important. He had started imagining the person he would be afterward. He didn't think so much about the kidnapping then, or even the kidnappers. It was all about him and the basement and what he did down there, who he would become, who he was meant to become. It was set and in motion. It was coming, Jason was sure of it. Not that he thought he was psychic or anything, it was just that this big thing was coming, so big he could feel it, and he had thought it through and whatever happened, he was going to be ready.

He stumbles and stops. He is almost gasping, smelling the sweat on his neck, the dust on the road, the acrid breeze from the eucalyptus trees past the stand of old-growth stunted apple trees around the curve. He leans forward, stretching his back, and straightens to watch a turkey buzzard circling the hill to his left. No hurry. It is only half a mile to his mom's place, two twists in the road and an uphill grade. Jason shakes his head. He knows this road in its whole length, two and a half miles and every decrepit house along the way, every crumbling garage and leaning fence. Of course, everyone here also knows him, which is sometimes more than he can stand. But somewhere someone who does not know him is coming along, and they will change everything. He nods and resumes a steady pace. Everything will be made over— and he will never know when or why. It will be a mystery.

He thinks of the basement room, that dim space with the windows boarded over. Nothing much will be down there, but he won't need much. He would love a piano, of course, but a guitar is more the kind of thing you might find in a basement. Nothing fancy. Some dented old acoustic. Jason thinks about it, the throw-away object he will use. God knows what he will have to do to tune the thing. Not likely to be any help in the junk people keep in basements. But there will be paper or notebooks. The notebooks will have pages marked up, of course, but he can work around that, use the backs of pages or something. It is what he creates in the silence that will need to be written down, the songs or poems. Lyrics. He will write it all down—easy to imagine that—him singing to himself in the quiet. The pencil marks along the pages. Of course his music notation sucks. He's never been too good at that. He sighs and stops again.

Maybe there will be a recorder—some old thing probably. A little old tape recorder, not a good digital. But hey it will get the job done. He smiles and hears above him the turkey buzzard's awkward call. Ugly sound from an ugly bird. He watches a big white pickup truck drive slowly up and past him. Big metal locks clamp down on the storage bin at the front of the truck bed.

Connie's boyfriend, Grange, told Jason you could bust most of those locks with the right chisel and mallet. "It's all in the angle. Got to hit it right."

Jason has a chisel in his backpack but no mallet. He licks his lips and resumes his slow hike between the ditch and the road. You got to have the right stuff to get anything done. Unless you are lucky or have an edge.

Famous is the way to go, he thinks. You get stuff once you are famous.

Jason wipes sweat off his neck as he walks and imagines it again—the reporter, the camera, the intensity of the lights, the intensity of his genius. It will take time, but he will figure it out. Maybe it won't be music. Maybe it will be words. He's damn good with words, not like those assholes at school who talk all the time. He knows the value of words, keeps them in his head, not always spilling them out like they mean nothing. He doesn't have to tell what he knows. He just knows—lyrics and poetry and all that stuff. Good poetry, he tells himself. Not that crap they want him to read in school. Kind of stuff makes your neck go stiff, that kind of poetry, that's what he likes. He looks at the dust on his hand, sweat-darkened and spotted with little grey-green bits. Little nubbins of weeds and grass flung up with the dust as the trucks pass. He'll get on the computer tonight, look up all the words for grey-green. Emerald, olive-drab, unripe fruit, something or the other. Nothing too hard about getting the words right.

Jason wipes his hands on his jeans, enjoying the feel of the fabric under his palms. Truth is more important than how you tell it, he thinks. And he knows stuff, lots of stuff, secrets and stuff. He has stories.

Maybe that will be it, the stories he tells himself to pass the time. Movie scripts, plays, dialogues between characters that come and go when he is all gaunt and feverish. In the basement, they won't feed him much, so he will get all dramatic skinny and probably have lots of fever dreams. He'll write them down, everything. His hands will cramp and he'll go on writing, get up and pace back and forth and write some more. Pages on pages will pile up. He'll bathe his face in cool water and walk some more. He'll drink so much water his skin will clear up. His mom is always telling him that if he washed his face more, drank more water and yeah, and ate more vegetables, his skin would do that right away. Maybe she has a point. Maybe in the basement that's all they will give him. Vegetables and water—lots of water, 'cause you know they ain't gonna waste no greasy expensive stuff on no captive. No Coke, no potato chips, no Kentucky Fried Chicken.

Pure water and rivers of words. Jason grins and lengthens his stride. Maybe after a while he won't care what he eats, or he will learn to make an apple taste like a pie. That would be the kind of thing might happen. He could learn to eat imaginary meals and taste every bite—donuts and hot barbecue wings—and stay all skinny and pure. That would be something. He could teach people how to do that afterwards maybe. Some day he might run an ashram like the one his mama used to talk about.

The turkey buzzard swoops low and arcs downhill toward the river. Jason stops to watch its flight. A moment in time and the bird disappears. Things can change that fast. Anything could happen and you can't predict what might come along. But what he knows is that there won't be any distractions down in the basement, anything to get in the way. Cold walls and dim light and maybe just a shower. Might be it will only run cold water, but he can handle that. What he hates is tub baths, sitting in dirty water. No way there is not gonna be a shower in the basement, or, all right, maybe only a hose and a drain in the floor. But he knows he will bathe himself a lot 'cause what else will there be to do? 'Cept write what he knows and use the weights set. He laughs out loud. Maybe there won't be no weights, though every shed or garage he knows has some stacked in some corner or the other. If there's nothing like that in his basement, still there will be stuff, something he can use.

He grabs his backpack straps again and begins the uphill grade. His steps slow and he focuses on the notion of making do, figuring out what he will use. Stuff like old cans of paint or bundles of rebar or bricks left lying around. He'll Tarantino it all, laying on the concrete floor and pushing up and down over and over till his arms get all muscled, and his legs too. He'll push off against the wall or doorjamb or something. He's gonna be bored out of his mind. He'll get desperate. He'll be working out, running in place and lifting heavy things—whatever he finds. Yeah, he'll get pretty well muscled. He grins. That is how it will be. He's going to come out just amazing.

Jason looks up the road, quarter of a mile to his mom's turnoff. He's right at the spot where the old firebreak cuts uphill, right up to his dad's place. He can almost see around the redwoods along the hill up to the house. He won't be like his dad, he thinks, he won't waste his chances. He'll grab what comes and run with it. When he comes out of that basement, he'll be slick. That is what it is all gonna be. Slick and sure, and he will know how to manage it, not wind up housesitting for some crappy old guy wants you to carry stuff and keep an eye on the dogs.

Fuck it. Jason says it out loud. "Fuck it!" He's gonna come out of that basement Brad-Pitt handsome and ready for anything. He'll be ready, all soulful and quirky like that guy from the White Stripes, only he won't take himself too seriously. Everyone else will do that for him. He'll know how to behave.

Jason laughs out loud again. "Yeah," he says. Yeah.

Serious. Yes. That's the word. He is going to be seriously famous.

That's when his mom will realize how shitty she has treated him. Then his dad will hear about it, for sure—and maybe let him come back up to the house and hang out. Of course that creep that owns the property will be around too, but Jason knows it won't be scary like last time. He'll have all those muscles, and he will have gotten past being scared of small shit like grabby old guys and dads that don't give a shit.

It will be different. It will all be different. His mom and his dad will work it all out. His dad will be his manager, his mom will take over the press stuff. You got to have someone handle that stuff, and if the creepy guy comes round to stake some kind of claim, it won't be no big deal. Everyone will know how to handle him—what to believe and what to laugh at. He can almost hear his dad talking loud in his growly hoarse voice. He can hear him finally saying what he wanted him to say before.

"Jason didn't take nothing off you, old man. Look at him. What would he need off you?"

Yeah.

But maybe he will let the old guy hang around. Jason thinks about it, looking uphill and remembering. He gnaws at the nail on his left little finger.

Maybe not.

Why would he want that old bastard around?

He thinks about his dad, what he looks like now, all puffy and grey around the eyes with his hair so thin on top. His dad had this belly on him that he tries to hide under loose shirts, and he's always worried about money and stuff. That kind of old is embarrassing. After the basement though, his dad will be all different. He'll be old, but not so gross. He'll be more like Clint Eastwood old, craggy and wise. That's the notion, and his dad will have figured stuff out all that time worrying about Jason. Things will be different once he sees his son clear. Maybe he'll even own the property by then. The old guy can't live forever. Maybe he'll just give his dad the top of the hill as a kind of death tip. Might be it will turn out like that guy in Forestville a few years back, that black guy who got the thirty acres in the will of the man he worked for all that time.

That could happen. And then if his dad needs someone to

help him with things, Jason will be there. That bad leg will hurt his dad a lot by then, even though he will try not to show it. Jason could do stuff—carry things for him and give him a hand. Maybe that is how they work it out— all the anger and guilt and shame and resentment. He can see that too, hear how it will go, them finally talking.

"You had no business running off like that, leaving Mom and me, I was just a little kid."

"You don't know how it was, how desperate I had gotten. I couldn't take care of you the way I wanted to, and you know your mom. She was always telling me I was lazy and the world wasn't gonna wait for me to get myself together."

That was just the kind of thing his mom said all the time. Jason nods. His mom can be a real pain in the ass. He sees himself looking at his dad and trying to imagine how he had felt when he had left. Maybe his dad had left in order to get himself together, to try and make something of himself so he could come back and take good care of them. After all that time cold and miserable and hungry in the basement, he will be able to feel stuff differently. Even standing in the dust of the road he can imagine his dad looking at him with an open face. Maybe they could talk finally, and it would shift all the anger around.

Maybe his dad will get to the point where he can look at him and see Jason clearly, see how he became so strong in that basement. Maybe he will finally see himself in his son. Of course, like everyone, his dad will know the story, how the kidnappers beat him, and starved him, and how Jason endured everything and stood up to them. It will make stuff in his dad shift around. He will get all wet-eyed and ashamed of himself. Jason can see that—the moment between them as real as the interviewer and the cameras, the moment burning him right through to his backbone. He almost sobs out loud, but then stops himself. His eyes are closed. The wind is picking up the way it always does as the afternoon settles toward evening. There is a birdcall somewhere up in the trees, but Jason is inside seeing into what is coming, what has to come.

They will touch each other like men do. Men. Yeah. Maybe his dad will embrace him, say his name. Jason can see that. It is as clear as anything. That is how it is in stories, how it is in his head, how it could be.

Jason sways a little there by the side of the road in the sun's heat. His ears are ringing with electric cricket sounds, the buzzard's cries, and the movement of the wind. Still, he hears a vehicle coming and the sound of its tires on the gritty tarmac. Rock and redwood debris grinding into dust and crackling as the wheels turn into the bend. Jason can see that, the wheels revolving and grinding forward. He imagines the kidnapper's truck, white and thick like one of those big Dodge Fat Boys, but one with a camper on the back—just the thing for snatching a guy off the road. Slowly Jason lets his face relax into a lazy smile. He doesn't look back. He keeps his eyes forward. His mom is always telling him to stop living in a dream, to be in the real world. But this is the real world, the road and the truck and everything that is coming toward him.

Anything can happen any time.

Everything can change, and it is going to, any time now.

Any time.

Any time.

Now.

I've Got a Run

August Tarrier

She loved the lightning more than the thunder—that I remember. Thunder was a letdown, she said—it meant you were safe. There's a place called Lightning Alley, she said, somewhere in Florida, and she was going to move there.

The day they found her body, I muttered the same flinty prayer—*last, let her be the last*, the last barefoot girl left for dead in a ditch, the last one floating face up under the viaduct, the last mouth bloody with missing teeth, the last one to cross the street alone, the last pair of drawers tangled in the dying leaves, the last broken bone.

The day they found the body the thermometer at Ray's Salvage hit 104, the foxes and chipmunks dove deeper into their burrows, and the post office closed. It was heat from hell, folks said, the underworld buckling up in fissures all over town, and the regulars at the Wagon Wheel claimed they couldn't get a seat, on account of everybody wanting a piece of the air conditioning.

The fat cop showed up that night, came into the only place anybody shows up on a Saturday night in Ridley, NE, but he, like me, was on shift. You could say I don't have a choice to be here, on account of I tend bar ever since I lost my job at Tompkins Elementary because of Covid. I was among the first to be laid off. Sheila says we're going back this fall, but I'll believe it when I see my first paycheck.

But even before Covid, I'd be here anyway, going on the wagon at the Wagon Wheel—another one of my "one lasts" before drawing up the drawbridge of sobriety. And where else would anyone want to be on this day of blasted heat?

There's only ever been two cops I've seen out here, the fat one and the thin one, and the thin one at least pretends to do his job. The fat one was phoning it in, even when he was looking right at you. He didn't need to tell me she'd been raped and strangled, 'cause what else would it be. I told him I didn't know her, but that I'd seen her around. He grinned at me, leaned up against the counter, and nodded, which meant, give me a shot of the best you got. He had one of those flip notebooks that cops carry, and he laid it on the bar as he picked up his shot. I saw what he'd written there, in block letters, scrawled—nobody learns penmanship anymore: "Whose gonna claim the body."

Whose.

I wanted to cry. I mean, talk about insult to injury, here she was dead, but how could a body expect any kind of decent treatment when the dumbfuck in charge doesn't know the difference between a pronoun and a contraction. I've said it a hundred times, *I've shed my last tear*—and so I don't cry, I put the kettle on and even in this heat I let it boil, I let the vapor rise. Tea because of 12 Steps—at least until I get here and can nip and sip my way through my shift. Unless I've got to bust out my stash of Nar-Can—then it's a night to get wasted with the rest of them.

She was here the night it happened, and if the cop or anybody in this whole friggin' county gave a shit, I would have told them. Soon as I saw that runner, I knew it was her. I know that hole, the way it rubs when you walk, the way it gives, and then that pair is ruined. If she had looked, she would have seen me looking.

I've got a run. I heard her say it, I heard her laugh.

I looked away: I knew my ghosts couldn't talk to her ghosts. Him—he was ordinary.

If anyone gave a shit, I'd tell them this story. I watched as he approached her, carefully, leaning in her direction. I saw her pull back, waiting to be cajoled closer. It didn't take long before she moved out of the shadows into the light, out of her corner seat, revolving once on the stool, as if to prove how easily she could still spin back into her own orbit and slip away.

Her name was Gloria. All I could see of her was a glint of silver—chandelier earrings—sweep of dark hair, blackened lashes, cracked crowded teeth, the kind of tumbledown teeth that make you think she could have been pretty if someone had thought to give her braces.

The guy, he was no skeevier than the next. A trucker maybe, or one of those dudes who sits around a mattress showroom all day waiting for someone to walk in. But there was something: half his pinky missing on his left hand. Now wouldn't that be an identifying detail to maybe catch this mofo? But nobody's going to do shit about another dead girl.

Gloria was good at small talk, she knew how to toss her head back and smile with her mouth even when her eyes weren't buying any of it. She wasn't radiant, not in the way that attracts all the stares, but she was welcoming.

As the night wore on, she was sandbagged in with this one gent, and then the spotlight dimmed. I could sense laughter and movement. I want to say he left fingerprints on her cold pale arms, I want to say he danced her right up against the jukebox, I want to say that the urge to warn her itched at me, it prickled on my skin like wool.

But there wasn't anything like that. Just his back—a suede jacket, the seal slick head, the porpoise bark of the laugh. From time to time, I could see the hand reach for the glass; I want to say he smeared bulbous prints on the glass, but the hand was mild, at least as far as I could see, and it did nothing more than grasp and pour the bubbles down. His back was to me the whole time, but still: I could have told them of the slicked back hair, the hand grasping the glass, the ragged pinky, the piss-yellow bubbles in the glass.

Occasionally, I heard a high gasp and then a gurgle of laughter, and she would tip her head forward, laughing hard. At those moments I loved her with a faraway admiring kind of love. But him, he was unmoved, as his fingers reached for the glass, drew it to him and the slick dark head tipped back.

At one point she stood up and hiked her leg onto the rung of the stool. She pivoted, leaning away from him, and then turned back, laughing.

I've got a run.

They left together—I saw them get up, but as they made their way to the door they were lost in the crowd and I couldn't see them again until they were in the parking lot. I got nothing but time here most nights and a nice big bay window. Him: Suede jacket, jeans, dark head. Her: tangled dark hair, heels. He opened the passenger side door for her, that counterfeit gesture. Then a glimpse of leg as she lowered herself into the seat, and the ladder running up to the thigh, white skin shining through shredded jet, and all I could think was that the arc of her life was already bending low. A patch of white throat, the crowded mouth seeming to grimace, as if she knew.

The slab of his back as he leaned down to shut the passenger door and then went around to the driver's side. I want to say there was menace—that he slammed the door, sped away, maybe spun some gravel as he pulled out. But he eased her into the seat, he shut the door gently.

I've got a run.

The past couple nights I dreamt of her. In my dream she was flying over ditches and gullies and canyons, and her story was rising up in her throat. But it's not a story I know, and aside from a paragraph in the paper (yep, we're that backward out here in Ridley, 162 miles from the county line, they still print obits in the *Tri-County News*, and the old timers still read 'em), I'll never know.

I still remember her grubby hand in mine. She was somebody's daughter, that I know. By the third grade, Gloria's Daddy had left her, and then her Mama too—these things a teacher knows, the way I know that Gloria wore the same dress for the entire third grade, until I went down to the Salvation Army and bought her a new one, red gingham with a tie at the waist, and made her put it on in the girls' bathroom, while she sobbed at having to take off the old one and tried to snatch it back out of the garbage where I tossed it.

If I was still a teacher, I would have quit teaching third grade the day they found Gloria's body in a culvert out on County Road 40 near Sawyer's Farm, where the dogwood bloomed and the oleander blossoms curled in the heat, where Sawyer used to keep horses, two palominos, a roan and a broken-down bay.

I still remember the evening I came upon that little girl playing in the street in her dirty dress, barefoot, after the streetlights had come on. I took that child by the hand and marched her straight through that field, where Old Tanner's retriever, Red, was rolling in the dirt.

"Where are your shoes?"

"Dunno."

"Have you done your homework?"

"Don't have any."

"It isn't proper for a girl to be out this late, all alone."

"My mama said I don't have to be home 'til dark."

I stopped and stood there, despite the chill and the child's bare feet and thin cotton dress, and pointed up to the heavens. "When the stars are out, you have to be inside."

Gloria dutifully studied the sky. "I only see but one star."

"Child, there are millions and millions of stars."

She stood there pondering for a moment. "If there's so many, how come I can't see them?"

"'Cause they're very far away."

"My daddy's far away."

I tugged on her hand and started marching her toward home. "They're much farther away than your Daddy is."

"They got stars where he is?"

No, they don't got stars in prison. But I didn't say that, not to an innocent child. But that's what you hear—you spend your life in prison you don't get to see the stars.

I carry with me a piece of every bedraggled girl. Can't help it. I remember their names and their grubby hands and their smudged faces and the tangled birds' nests of their hair. This grubby girl was no different than the others—no taller, no smarter, no prettier. And yet long after the third grade she remained one of the brightest in the firmament of my memory.

On days like this, when the heat shimmers in pockets and gullies, I remember her running in the knee-high grass amid the daisies and thistles big as fists and I light a candle and say a prayer for a child whose hopes were as thin as smoke.

The year Gloria turned fourteen, I'd sometimes see her in the picture window of the doughnut shop, powdered sugar sprinkled on her breast, inhaling the sweet yeasty crullers as she spun on the cracked crimson seat of a stool, arching her back, rolling her eyes, giggling as she licked the powder off her lips.

Then she disappeared for the longest time, and I figured she'd moved away or maybe she was already dead. But then I started seeing her at the Wagon Wheel. You don't have to look hard to see the regulars assembled here, the troubled souls, and Gloria, the troubled child, was suddenly here too, all grown up and troubled still, only now she seemed to be meeting trouble with a handful of aces, looking trouble right in the face, unable to resist the temptation to put her slender fingers around Trouble's thick neck and squeeze.

I didn't pay her any mind—I just couldn't. As I hurried past to bus a table or bang on the bathroom door and pray somebody wasn't dopesick in there, I'd catch a glimpse of dark hair swirling across a face I'd known decades earlier. *Say amen*, I'd mutter, and maybe bring it up in Meeting, but never with a name, just to say how scared I was of losing another one.

I've spent many a night praying that there would be no more girls like Gloria, with their snarled curls and nails bitten to the quick, and their dirty knees and elbows, and their darting eyes, no more stringy-haired girls in tattered dresses who lived under only one star.

I've done everything I can to scrub the image of her lying in the ditch, several inches of groundwater seeping in around her as the deer sniff her cold fingers, but even the top-shelf shit won't get me far enough gone for that.

These days I pray that there will come a day when it all ends, just quick like that, just snuff it all out—the last robin, the last meadow grouse, the last buttercup. The last bird of summer plucking berries from the last bush, the last monarch grazing a treetop before migrating to Mexico. I pray for a day when even the cicadas stop, and the angels bend down with their harps, if there are such things as angels (and most days I believe there are) because their music is the only thing that could make me cry again, now that I've got no tears left.

I think the fat cop's name was Frank, or maybe Joe, one of those names that nobody ever remembers. He was sitting near the window, squeezed in with Petey Williams and Leroy Stauffer. I came out from behind the bar and I marched over there, all business. I could see the flip pad on the table, and as I got closer, I could see it was just the same words, he'd added nothing—"Whose gonna claim the body?"

I stood over him and the other two, over all the bodies packed into the bar, and the hum of words rising in the heat, and they stopped talking and stared up at me, and because nothing surprises me anymore, I grabbed the pen right out of the cop's hand, I turned that pad in my direction, and I conjured all the coltish third-grade girls half out of their desks wiggling their arms high—*me, me, call on me!* as I wrote, *Who is, Who is, Who is.*

Jackpots Only

Michael Darcher

Once he sees her through the torn screen door, Leonard assumes a smile, enters the trailer without invitation. She is seated, legs crossed, one raised arm holding a white filtered cigarette that sports a Peter Pan collar of red lipstick. She wears a collarless, electric pink blouse elasticized at every port of entry, a white, plastic belt four inches wide, blue jeans rolled up in pirate cuffs, white go-go boots. Leonard maintains his smile but he is disappointed that she is still in full make-up, still has her hair done up in a beehive. He had hoped to see a different version of Jackie than the one she displays at the casino.

"You didn't bring any beer?" she says. "I thought blackjack dealers made good money."

"I meant to," he says, but it's a lie. A mile away at the Aces Oasis cabaret bar, Alex waits for him with two female tourists and four tickets to the Pointer Sisters cocktail show. Leonard knows what Jackie is expecting, but he plans to stay just long enough to sell her his earrings. "I didn't know what brand you drink," he says. This deal is strictly cash and dash.

"I don't have a brand. I take whatever fits." She lights another cigarette but leaves the room without it.

Leonard surveys the trailer surprised at how cavernous it seems. He studies each furnishing: the pine-board veneer that serves as wallpaper, the twin couches both deeply soiled, a shriveled aloe plant, brass elephant head book ends that hold no books, a shadeless lamp, an empty wooden coffee table painted shiny red, a paint-splattered magazine rack full of torn, dated fan club magazines. Most of all, he notices the day-glo velveteen picture of Cher that hangs above the console. Adorned in a fringed cowhide blouse and a beaded headband, Cher sits in a canoe, arms crossed and lips parted in delicious privity, suggesting to him she has a secret she just might divulge.

Leonard checks his watch. Where is she? He drags the red table over to a couch wondering why every piece of furniture has been pushed against a wall. He unhinges the elk horn clips of his leather case and lets it unfold. He holds it at arm's length like a calendar, then jostles the case until the dozen sets of earrings hang untangled. He sets the display in the center of the table. He studies each pair, wonders which ones she will buy.

The earrings weren't his idea. It was his sister who came home wearing the Jock Scott he had abandoned after inadvertently clipping the barb. "This is too cool," she said. Her friends thought so, too, and offered to pay Leonard for his creations although some of them, the punks, asked him not to clip the barbs. A crafts show jeweler also found his flies "conceptual." That winter, he tied a thousand flies that would never find water. By Memorial Day, he had made enough money to leave Manchester.

His plan was to fish the California Sierra, then the blue ribbons up in Montana, but a blown piston rod and a bad run of cards in Reno forced him to get a job in the slot department at the Aces Oasis. The indifference his earrings received surprised him, but only briefly. The Blue Duns and Bitch Creek Nymphs, flies he had brought with him from New Hampshire, didn't sell well in the casino so he created garish, fictitious flies that did. These new earrings became the rage among the cocktail hostesses and women dealers, one of whom pulled strings to get him into a dealing school in return for three pairs.

After class at the bar, he boasted to the three other guys in his 21 training school, who were keenly aware of the attention Leonard received, that it took a new fly to hook a new fish. What Leonard didn't tell them was that these women who had initially regarded him as moody and odd now found him sensitive and smart. In their eyes, Leonard was an artist. Best of all, the earrings became the pick-up lines he had never mastered at Dartmouth. Now Leonard always keeps a pair on his person. In his sports coat lie a pair of feathered beauties he'll use tonight to reel in his half of the tourists.

"Here you go, Cash Daddy," Jackie says and thrusts a Coors at him, keeping the Schlitz for herself. She places a bowl of stick pretzels on the coffee table and sits beside him, closer than she has to. "Fab!" she says and plucks free the pair he thinks are the most tawdry.

He knows he is staring at her excessive make-up, knows that she knows, but still he cannot avert his eyes from her eye shadow. The iridescence reminds him of fish scales. In her, he sees the eyes of an old, tired stockie that has somehow survived, become indigenous. He guesses that she is a good five years older than him, thirty, maybe thirty-one.

"Do you fish?"

"No," she says. "I don't like being near water."

Leonard tries a different cast. "Have you lived here long?"

"Six months. Is that long?"

"This is only the second mobile home I've ever been in," he tells her. "The first one was an office on a used car lot. I liked the car but I didn't like the salesman, so I didn't buy the car."

She looks at him then drops the earrings to the display. She selects another pair and holds them up to the light. "How much did you say these cost?"

Her eye shadow is the color of an Earl Scheib paint job his parents once got on the family Ford. "Still $29.95," he says, three times their actual price. She lets this pair as well plummet to the case.

This afternoon, Leonard was in the casino to sell a pair to a day shift roulette dealer and to visit with a friend in the slot department he hadn't seen since he'd jumped to swing shift and begun dealing cards. Jackie wasn't someone he'd planned on seeing. They hadn't worked together that long. And he usually avoided women who were taller than him. But the thrust of her chest into his had seemed intentional. When she beckoned him to follow her down a row of slot machines, he did.

"What's in the case?" she asked as she made her way down the aisle to a woman seated on a stool between two slot machines. Leonard felt foolish trailing her. He hoped none of the nearby day shift dealers were watching.

"This one's jammed," the woman on the stool said, pointing to one slot machine while feeding quarters into another.

"Guess what?" Jackie said. She motioned for Leonard to open his case. "This is the last day I'll ever have to sell coin rolls out of this stupid apron. Starting tomorrow, I'll just be paying off jackpots and doing the dinky repair stuff on the machines. No more old broads poking me in the ribs when they want change. Starting tomorrow, I'm jackpots only."

She fiddled momentarily with the coin slot. "You've jammed the machine," she told the woman. "I'll have to call a JPO."

"Why can't you fix it?"

"If I could, I would," Jackie said and then remembered. "Tomorrow, I will be able to fix it."

"That won't do," the woman said. "We're leaving tomorrow."

"Then you got a problem," Jackie said. The woman's good machine paid out ten quarters.

"Cherries, always cherries," the woman said. "I hate cherries."

"You got two problems," Jackie said and turned to examine Leonard's earrings, and again, he thought, pushed herself into him.

"Come here," she ordered as she walked by two service lights, past two surprised customers who would have to buy their rolls of quarters from someone else.

Leonard slowed down when he saw that she was leading

him to Lois, her roommate. He stopped altogether when he saw the roulette dealer's disparaging look. He heard Jackie calling his name. He sighed hard and stared down the dealer. She had no right to be offended. It was the slot department who had to bear the brunt of Jackie and Lois' oddity. As a slot floorman, he'd heard the others laugh at Lois' acrylic blond wig, her make-up, the way she wore her change apron slung below her gut like a bandito. He had heard the cashiers express their disbelief that someone her size would wear stretch pants. "Miss Piggy" they called her. He sensed that they disliked Jackie even more because they knew that despite the capri pants, the stiletto heels, the beehive hair-do, she was still an attraction, and it was only a matter of time until she advanced to a better job in another department.

"Show Lois," Jackie said. Ceremoniously, he opened the jaws of the jewelry case that contained three sets of earrings.

"Yeah, so?" Lois said.

"I think they're fab," Jackie said. "I want a pair."

"I don't," Lois said and walked away.

"I do," Jackie said. She shut her eyes for a full second, enough time for Leonard to compare her green eye shadow with her red lipstick. Merry Christmas, he thought.

"The money's at my house," she said.

Leonard smiled. He could interpret that line. He laughed and dismissed the notion, but afterward, he went home and crafted eight new pairs.

He cannot hear the wind but from his seat in the living room, Leonard feels it, sees it pressing into the trailer walls. He wonders now if it's the wind that has pushed each piece of furniture like a tumbleweed against the wall where it can go no further. "I feel like I'm being digested," he says.

She sits stiffly, gazing not at him but at velveteen Cher over his shoulder.

"The wind. This trailer. This room. It's churning."

"What are you talking about?" she says.

He shakes his beer can, wishes it was empty. "Doesn't living in a trailer get to you?"

"Everything gets to me after a while."

"How many rooms are there anyway?"

"Four, if you count all this as one room and don't count the bathroom."

"That's it," he says. "Four rooms, four stomachs. We're inside a cow. We're nothing but cud."

Jackie raises a penciled eyebrow. She looks at Leonard with concern.

"Have you ever milked a cow?" he asks.

"What's that supposed to mean?"

"Didn't you grow up on a farm?" It's just a guess.

"Yeah," she says. "A funny farm."

"Aren't you from Modesto or Bakersfield or some place like that?"

"I don't remember."

"I had an ant farm once," he says. "But all the ants died. I put new ants in but they died, too. They all crawled to the bottom and died. It took me a week to shake them through the passages and get them all to the top. It was like owning a labyrinth. I used to feel that way about our slot section. Luck runs through the casino like a Minotaur, don't you think?"

Jackie extends the same raised eyebrow. "I'm going to take a piss," she says.

Make sure you put it back, he wants to tell her but fears she won't see the humor in that either. He checks his watch, knowing by now Alex and the two women are standing in line for the show and wondering where he is. He knows he could drain his beer, gather his valise and be out the door before she returns, but he doesn't. There's unfinished business here, he realizes, and it's not just the earrings.

He eyes the day-glo Cher and sinks further into the couch.

Jackie isn't like the women dealers. With her, his elliptical words and seductive earrings have been nothing but bullets fired into the sky. It's situations, Leonard knows, not people, that he's learned to master. Recognize desire and offer it as bait. His earrings have taught him that. But tonight, inside this mobile home, there's nothing familiar. And that's the allure.

Leonard twirls a set of earrings, lets them drop to the table like he saw her do. He shakes his display, seeing how many sets he can snarl. His choice is simple. He can fish from his usual spot and catch nothing. Or he can toss all his flies in the river and jump in after them, letting the river, her river, carry him downstream and wash him onto another bank, to the one place where he just might limit out.

Leonard chooses Plan B.

And thinks Leonard: I'll see this woman exposed. I'll make her eyes turn all new shades of green. I'll know her.

She returns with a bottle of Bud and a can of Hamm's.

"You really don't have a brand, do you?"

"I don't have time to look," she says. "What's the difference? I got them free. You get them free. What are you, a beer snob?"

He avoids her eyes. He counts the sets of earrings inside the valise, studies the ones he made just for her. "Where's Lois tonight?"

"At work, I hope. It's too quiet. Do you like music?"

"Are the Kennedys gun-shy?"

She walks past him to the console unable, or unwilling he thinks, to respond to his glibness. Fair enough. It's supposed to be her show anyway, not his.

When she faces him, holding out record albums as if they were steering wheels, studying their titles with no concern about scratching or smudging them, Leonard feels that he is being offered something. He notices that she has removed her rouge and eye shadow. The eyelashes and lipstick remain, but the absence of other coloring makes her look younger. He watches her stack four albums on the spool. He hears the control arm slide over the top LP. The first album drops. He is surprised how unscratched this version of *Halfbreed* sounds.

"You really like Cher, don't you?"

"I adore her," she says and picks a new set of earrings to finger. "I named my daughter after hers. Wouldn't it be neat if they became friends someday?"

"You have a daughter?"

Jackie nods solemnly. "Chastity. She's six."

"She's not here, is she?"

"No." She draws a cigarette from a red vinyl case. She murmurs the lyrics as she lights up.

"Why Cher?"

"I love her hair," Jackie says and strokes her own. "I love her nose, those teeth, everything about her. I admire her taste in younger men. I really like the way she dresses. It's cool. Before Chastity, I used to dress like that."

"Why?"

She impales him with a look. "Why does anybody do anything? The way I see it, those who got it, show it. Those who don't, hide it." She pulls at her sleeves. Leonard sees the lines on her arms that the elastic has made.

He tries to guess when this album was first released. He wonders what the appeal was, tries to imagine what a Cher concert was like, wonders who went, what they looked like, what the original fans took for a buzz. "You're an anachronism," he tells her.

She blows out distasteful smoke. "I have no idea what you're talking about," she says. "I'm not that complicated."

He swallows half his beer and asks her to dance.

She offers him her erect arm then draws him slowly to her. She wants to lead and he lets her. He hated it in the seventh grade, but tonight it feels good to dance with someone taller. They dance in a slow, continuous circle. He likes it that her perfume smells like jello. It no longer matters that she is different from the others. What matters is that she is different from him.

They dance through the silence between songs. They swirl slowly, cheek to cheek, chest to chest, right into *I Got You, Babe*. She does not recoil when he kisses her ear.

"If only I could get a dealing job," she says. "If I can make some money, show them I can hold a job, then maybe I can get my daughter back."

"Who's got your daughter?"

"The state."

He doesn't ask which one. "Where's your husband?" he asks instead.

"How would I know? I never had one." She stops dancing.

"Sorry. I meant the father."

She fishes for a cigarette.

"So where's the father?"

"How the hell should I know?" she says and goes for her can of beer. "He could still be in this town for all I know. Does it matter?" She looks at her cigarette, at the earrings, at him. "This beer sucks," she says. "I'm getting another."

Leonard sits down in his same spot. He rests his feet on the coffee table and shakes his display. He notices that one pair is missing.

The entire side of an album plays before she returns. She is now dressed in a pink, fluffy bathrobe and carries with her two jelly jars full of wine. He thinks that she's been crying. A single strand of stiff, lacquered hair hangs free from her beehive. He sees that she has removed more make-up, and it occurs to him that he is witnessing some sort of reverse metamorphosis, a time lapse film being rewound, a video in which the butterfly forsakes its luster and returns to the cocoon. Now she looks his age, a disturbing thought.

"Dance with me," he says but she wants to wait for a fast song. She is chain smoking.

Leonard drinks, shudders. "What is this?"

"MD 20/20. I'm out of beer."

He sets down the jar, picks up the valise. "Pick a pair," he says. "Try them on."

Without hesitation, she pulls a pair of Adult Damsels and hooks them both to one ear.

"Good. You needed color."

"I got color," she says. "I got three tattoos. All cherries. I went out and got them when I found out about Cher's tattoos."

He braces himself, then swallows more wine. "Show me," he says.

"This'll do," she says and stands up to a new song.

So does Leonard. La da da de dee. She gyrates in a succession of dances, calling out the name of each one: the Fish, the Hully Gully, the Boog-a-loo, the Skate, the Shake. He tries to mimic her. La da da de dah. As soon as he does, she switches to a new dance.

It's the last song on the last album and the silence that follows seems to bother her. She shakes when lighting a filterless cigarette from a fresh pack.

"God damn it," she says. "He never should have left."

"Who?"

She looks at him angrily. "Sonny."

"How do you know it was his idea?"

"How do I know?" She walks overs to the magazine rack and grabs a handful of magazines. Each one that she throws at him has Cher on the cover. "I know," she says. "Besides, it's always the guy."

Leonard drinks the last of his Mogen David and goes to the kitchen to pour himself another. He hears footsteps and braces, thinks that Jackie, enraged, is coming after him. He turns but she is nowhere.

He stares at his own reflection in the kitchen window. He laughs at his fear. Does she want him to be her guy? He hears the wind and looks outside for evidence, but sees no trembling leaves, no raised dust, no tumbleweeds. There are no signs of weather except the sound. Again, he catches his reflection. He wonders if Alex and the tourist women will dance the Hully Gully tonight.

Gone now are all vestiges of make-up. She has removed her eyelashes and, Leonard notices, his earrings. She has let down her hair. Stiff and straight, it falls down to her waist. Thick bangs now cover her forehead, reaching almost to her eyebrows. In a small way, she does remind him of Cher.

"Show me your tattoos."

She walks out of the kitchen to the console to play a new stack of records. She brings back her jar and her cigarettes.

"Show me."

"I'll show you one," she says without affection. She separates the top of her robe, revealing her right areola that has been colored blood red and given a cherry rump and a green stem that curls toward her sternum.

Leonard reaches to touch it.

"No," she says and covers herself.

He recognizes the music. "Dance?" he asks at the next slow song.

"They used to drive his and her pink Mustangs," she says. "They used to do everything together."

In her arms, under her lead, again he finds contentment. They dance and linger in embrace after song's end. This time, it's Leonard who breaks free. He flashes her his biggest set of dolphin eyes. She pauses only to grab a fresh pack of cigarettes before allowing herself to be led down the hallway. "This one," she says at the second door and closes it behind them.

In the dull moonlight, his eyes never leave her. She's got Cher's teeth, he thinks. And her hair, though he wishes that she'd kept it up in a beehive because now she looks like other women. He wants to ask her about Sonny. He wants to learn why any man would leave Cher, but he doesn't. He's afraid she'll see the Sonny in him.

He knows his hands are ice so he is careful where he puts them. Her hair feels fake. Doll's hair. He draws her closer. Her hair feels strange, but her kisses stranger. Limp, exaggerated, offered in amateur passion.

"How old are you?" he asks.

"Twenty-one."

"Blackjack," he says. When she doesn't respond, he kisses her and tastes cigarette smoke.

"Jackie can't be your real name."

"It's Jack. Nice name to give to a girl, huh? I think my parents wanted a boy."

"It could have been worse," he says. "In China, they toss female babies into the gutter like trout heads, or else torture and maim them for life by boxing their feet. At least they did until the Boxer Rebellion."

He hears her sigh and realizes he's doing it again, trolling his stream, not hers. So he makes his move.

He is refused. She is willing to kiss and be held but not caressed, and after his third wave of passion defeats him with a single "Please" before rolling away to her edge of the bed.

"Fabulous," Leonard mutters. He props himself against the headboard and tries to catch a glimpse of her face. He looks for a flaw in her complexion, a birthmark, a blemish, anything that will make her less winning. But the absence of light and color cleanses her. Eyes closed, she is innocent. Pure. His anger dissipates. He wonders how many more years her pillow will erase from her face, wonders how complete her metamorphosis will be.

He scans the room for a clock, knowing it's too late to make the Pointer Sisters show. He thinks about leaving anyway, but remembers he hasn't collected for the earrings. He can get that much at least. "Jackie," he whispers, but she is fast asleep.

He is almost asleep when he hears a door being slammed. A second slam brings him upright. He remembers where he is and for a horrifying moment, wonders if Chastity's father is the one making all the noise. He stares at Jackie who is asleep, wonders if he'll fight for her honor. He watches her thread her fingers, prayer-like. If she has heard anything, she does not let on.

A third slam and now the whole trailer shakes.

The fourth slam is softer, muted. It sounds like someone knocking on their door.

"Who's there?" Leonard asks. He looks at Jackie for help. "Who's there?" he asks again before a more horrifying thought seizes him. Perhaps it's Lois, drunk and amorous, preparing to join them. He grips the top of the covers. He has often dreamed of a threesome. But not this one. Not tonight.

He hopes whoever is out there will go away but the next slam, coming a minute later, is the loudest yet.

"Who's there?" he asks.

The next slam, louder still, rouses him out of bed. He kicks around the rug but can't find his pants.

Another slam.

"Screw it," he says and bounds into the hallway. Through the gauzy light extending from the kitchen window, he spots a white plastic belt on the hallway floor. He raps the perforated end around his palm. He notices that the front door is open.

"Who's out there?" he asks, swinging the belt like a sling. "Who's there?" he shouts, leaping into the kitchen.

No one is there. Not under the kitchen table, not in the front closet, not kneeling behind the console. Leonard walks up to the open door. He peers out at the starless sky, at the rows of unlit condos that loom above the trailer park. "Who's there?" he wants to know.

He locks the door, walks to the bathroom. Unwilling to let go of the belt, he uses his left hand to pee, stares into the mirror imagining his own tattoos. He envisions a stack of one hundred dollar chips needled into his breast. Or an ace and a face *the queen of hearts?* etched on his bicep. Maybe a pair of rolling dice tumbling across his knuckles. He swings the bathroom door out of his way. Boldly, he opens the door to the first bedroom and peers in.

There is nothing in there that belongs to Lois. No bed. No bureau or piles of cast off clothes. The room is empty except for a hair dryer, the dome and seat type he's seen in beauty parlors.

He tiptoes down to the only other door. He hesitates, then opens it, but all he finds is a cement basin and a washer and dryer. He retreats to the living room and feels the front of both couches. Neither one is a sleeper.

When he returns to her room, the light is on and Jackie is awake, smoking a cigarette.

"Was that you?" she asks.

"No."

"What's with the belt?" she asks but he won't tell her.

"You got scared, didn't you?" she says and laughs smoke.

"No… Yes."

"What are you so scared of?"

"I don't know," he says and fumbles to unravel the belt. "I thought there was someone out there."

"There probably was."

He wonders if he is safer in or out of bed.

"You're afraid of the dark," she says on her way out of the room. "That's sweet."

I know your secret, he thinks, but the realization offers him no comfort. It pushes into him like the wind he can feel prodding the trailer walls.

When she returns, he sees a second tattoo. It lies on the inside of her left thigh. It, too, is a cherry of equal size to the first. "Cherries, always cherries," he says.

She draws herself to him and allows his hands full range of her. He is pleased that she does not shrink when reaching past him for the light.

"Can we leave it on?" he asks.

"Cool!" she says and keeps saying the word as if to remind herself.

Her distraction does not deter him. His hands touch every-where, especially her tattoos. He is disappointed that the dyed skin feels no different. Still, his hands light on the cherries like bees, then trace other parts of her, rapt, impatient, always re-turning to the cherries.

"Slow down," she says. "It's all right here."

Leonard obeys. He does not tell her he is searching for the third tattoo.

Leonard wakes up alone. Beyond the closed door, he hears run-ning water, raised voices, smells coffee. He kneels on the bed and looks out the window for evidence of wind. Nothing shimmers. He dresses and for laughs, fastens the white belt around his waist.

At the kitchen table, Lois stares into a make-up mirror and applies mascara to newly fastened eyelashes. Across the table, Jackie primps in front of her own mirror. She dabs at her eyelids with a finger of iridescent goo. Her face is thick with make-up. Her hair is loosely stacked. Leonard removes the white belt. Only Lois notices.

"Morning," he says and sits in the chair between them. Lois moves away her mirror and chair.

"Thanks," Leonard says, grateful for the room. Lois glares and moves away even further.

"Would you like some coffee?" Jackie asks.

"Yes, please," and then, "I'll get it" when Jackie makes no attempt to serve him.

From the kitchen, he hears Lois say, "That's him? That makes me feel even worse." He watches Jackie light two cigarettes and hand Lois one.

"You'll get over it," she tells Lois. "You always do."

"But why do you have to wave it in my face?" Lois asks. "Why can't you ever go over to their place?"

"I told you on Day One," Jackie says. "I'm a gypsy. I'm a tramp. I'm a thief. Help me with my hair, will you?"

He absorbs Lois' stare when she rises and stands behind Jackie, watches her caress Jackie's shoulders. "Do you think I like taking a taxi home?" he hears Lois ask. "You think I like sleeping in someone else's car?"

"You could have slept on the couch," Jackie says.

"And listen all night to you and someone else? No thanks."

He thinks about leaving but decides that would be something the old Leonard, not the Plan B Leonard would do, so he returns to the table with a full cup of coffee and endures Lois' disapproval. For thirty-five minutes, he drinks instant coffee and watches them pin, pluck, smear, curl, comb, dab, gloss, spray, spritz, and pat until they are butterflies again. Until they are what he and everyone else at the casino are used to seeing, expect to see, and Leonard realizes that he has been waiting to witness their return all along. That until this moment, he has been trespassing. Poaching.

"Do me," he says.

"What?"

"Make me over," he says to Jackie. "I need color, too."

It's Lois who slides over her make-up tray and begins applying foundation in steady swipes. Leonard can detect no pattern in her application. Each dab seems intentionally arbitrary and although he thinks she is having fun at his expense, he lets her apply a round of blush. He closes his eyes, which Lois immediately goes after with fingers of eye shadow, and imagines himself a rainbow trout nestled in cool morning mud. When he opens his eyes, Lois stops, puts everything away. Leonard beams and feels the crevices his smile has just made. He looks to Jackie for approval, but she is in the kitchen hunched over a bowl of cold cereal and a magazine. She has been there all along.

He stands beside her until she has no choice but to look. "What do you think?" he asks.

"I *don't* think," she says, emptying the box of cereal onto the countertop. "I don't think you should be here." She passes her hand through the mound of flakes, searching vainly for the prize.

Leonard goes for his sports jacket and valise that one of them has placed by the door. He wants to open the case to see how many pairs are missing. Instead, he asks, "How many sets did you decide to take?"

Jackie and Lois laugh at this. Lois points to the living room. To Cher. Jackie stands and tugs at her blouse. She checks her contours in a mirror.

"You look nice," Lois says.

"I feel great," Jackie says.

"What about my earrings?" Leonard says.

"No more change apron," Jackie says. "Starting today, I, Jackie Pratt, am jackpots only. Yes!"

Door open, he waves to her in small swipes, then to Lois, then to Cher, who he notices is wearing a Damsel in her right ear.

In the sunlight, the condos seem more distant. Slowly, he backs out of the driveway careful not to raise any dust. He wants to leave it all untouched, leave no evidence of himself. Catch and release. He avoids catching his reflection in the rear view mirror, but he can't avoid the reek that's new to his upholstery so he yields to it. He inhales raspberry jello, deeply this time, and thinks about going fishing. He decides that when he gets home, he'll tie as many flies as are missing from his valise. Real flies that will catch real fish. Then he'll wash his face, locate his fishing license and a fly rod, and walk down to the Truckee River. He needs to be near water.

The Grass Jesus Walked On

Elizabeth Bruce

"One dollar," young Earl C. Calder said and looked at the farmer before him transfixed on the small, blue vial Earl held in his hand.

Earl didn't blink in the mid-day sun, all 110 pounds of himself holding steady next to Ida. The vial of elixir they had emptied the night before still floated through him, but he didn't flinch, not Madam Wilma T.'s son, born in a brothel and groomed for greatness.

"One dollar," he said again and tapped the inky blue container. "This here blade of grass is the real thing, friend. Walked on by the Savior himself, Jesus Christ, the Son of God, one thousand eight hundred and sixty-six years ago on his way to the cross."

Beside him, young Ida C. Morrow leaned her lithe body forward, holding out a weathered moccasin they'd found in the peddler's belongings and patting its underside. "Sanctified," she said, in her soft New Orleans' murmur, "by the sole of He who died for our sins."

She tilted her head down and smiled sweetly the way Madam Wilma had insisted the girls do at the brothel, especially the new ones fresh from their stations in the kitchen or laundry or sewing circles where they earned their keep until they reached their age of consent, a whole 13 years of age in New Orleans according to the Napoleonic Code in 1866. "Sweetness, girls. Sweetness sells," the Madam would say. "Sweetness brings Papa Bear to the honey pot, and you, my sweets, are the sweetest honey pots in all of Orleans Parish.

Ida closed her eyes and shook her head. She steadied herself at the edge of the wagon. Her dark curls bounced, and a stray strand plastered itself in the sweat along her pale pink temple. Sweetness, she thought, and suddenly she felt sick again, sick like she'd felt the whole of her 12th year watching her 13th birthday grow closer and closer.

The elixir she'd drunk with Earl the night before welled up in her, and Ida forced a swallow. She hadn't wanted any of it in Wilma T.'s employ, not the long hours in the kitchen ducking Cook's ire, not the leers of the rich old men who came to the brothel waiting, waiting for the youngest girls to ripen into service, and most especially she hadn't wanted the fawning, liquor-laced embrace of the displaced old mayor, desperate to salvage his Southern manhood on the tiny bodies of Wilma T.'s youngest conscripts.

"Yes sir, touched by the Savior's soul," Earl's sing-songy refrain filtered through to Ida, and she smiled again, sweetly. The farmer and his lanky son were leaning into Earl now, ogling the blue vial he cupped in his hand, their curiosity ablaze. The blue of the bottle and the blue of Earl's eyes danced before her.

She had wanted Earl, though, this pretty-faced young man with the easy laugh and boyish swagger that had charmed his mother so. "Born to lead," the Madam had sworn, and for a quick flash Ida wondered if she were dreaming that he'd really gone and done it, broken free of his mama at last, broken the hold she had on the both of them.

They had fled, snuck out of the brothel in the wee hours when the errant husbands and preachers and foreign sailing men had crept back to their wives and parsonages and vessels, the fire of their manhood tamed for one more night. Even the piano player had gone to bed when Earl and Ida had slipped out the kitchen door, their meager possessions stuffed in an old satchel, and skittered down the empty cobblestones to the edge of the opium district, when they'd run across the peddler lying doped up and snoring outside a Chinese laundry.

Taking the wagon had been Ida's idea, and Earl had heartily

agreed. "Why, it's the perfect means of transport and disguise," he'd said, and they'd scratched a Bill of Sale on the back of a flea powder label that had fallen off one of the peddler's wares. "Sold," Ida had pronounced and stuffed a handful of Confederate dollars into the sleeping peddler's coat pocket, the worthless coin of rebellion, and off they'd gone, headed to Texas and a life unknown.

Leaning over the edge of that wagon, Earl C. Calder now lowered his voice to a gruff whisper. Ida strained to hear his proclamation to the farmer.

"Just one dollar, sir, for a piece of the sacred ground walked on by our Lord himself, yours to have and to hold here in Port Neches and wash away the sins of our souls." Earl waved the blue vial again before the grizzled face of the farmer, the wet spring mud of east Texas caked across his overalls.

"Young sins, brother," added Earl, lowering his voice like Ida's whisper. "Yours and mine and Ida's here. Sins of the father and sins of the son. Young or old as we are, we all have sins, mister," Earl said, and he knelt and placed his hand on the shoulder of the farmer's tall, scrawny son standing wide-eyed and smitten before Ida.

"Sold," said the farmer, and from somewhere deep in the pockets of his dungarees still stained with Confederate defeat, the farmer grabbed hold of a Yankee dollar, the wretched coin of capitulation, and gave it over to Ida perched between the boxes of elixirs and broad cloth and cast-iron kettles that had once been the stock in trade of a Connecticut peddler.

"Bless you, sir," said Ida, smiling kindly again, and she tucked the man's dollar into the pocket of her muslin skirt, frayed at the hemline and flecked with grass stains. She took the small blue vial from Earl's finger and handed it to the farmer. "May it bring you a lifetime of blessings from our Lord and Savior, Jesus Christ," she said. "The one and only son of God."

The farmer took the small bottle in his rough hands and brought it to his lips. "Thank you, lassie," he muttered, and laying his hand on the shoulder of the boy beside him, turned to go.

"Sir," Ida suddenly called to him but the farmer, unaccustomed perchance to being addressed as such, didn't turn. "Brother Believer," Ida called again and this time the man stopped and turned, and Ida scampered down from atop the peddler's wagon holding something.

"As a show of our appreciation, sir, we give you this switch dipped in the River Jordan by John the Baptist himself," Ida said, reaching out to hand the man a long slim twig stripped of leaves.

"Lest any wickedness descend upon your only son here," Earl added, rushing over to Ida's side, "as he wades into the perilous waters of manhood."

The farmer, startled perhaps by such magnanimity, stepped forward and took the switch and lowered it to his side. "Thank you kindly, younguns," he said, looking from Earl to Ida. "Ways of the world's a troublesome road, that's a true born fact."

And with that, the farmer laid his arm back across his son's back and the two of them strode off toward the mule-drawn wooden wagon beside the Opelousas Trail folks traveled on in these parts, cattlemen and preachers and immigrant folk, the same rough road Santa Ana had once walked on shackled and chained by triumphant Texans on a long walk of shame to New Orleans.

Earl turned and winked at Ida, who smiled and wiped away the Texas sweat on her brow. She lifted the hem of her skirt out of the dust and turned back to the wagon. Earl held out his hand and Ida took it as she stepped back up on to the wagon's seat.

Gently, Ida ran her hand over the leaflet that a drunk and defeated Confederate soldier, the right side of his body mangled, had left at the brothel, taking advantage of the Madame's soft spot for the fallen South. Ida had stuffed it in her apron pocket and shown it to Earl, and he had grinned and kissed Ida on the lips the way he'd done only once before, and Ida had blushed and Earl had blushed. And right then and there they'd sealed the deal of running off together.

They'd tacked the leaflet inside the peddler's wagon as soon as they headed out of New Orleans. "Great is Texas" read the pamphlet. *Great! Grand! Glorious! Ranchers Paradise, Cheap Land—Low Taxes!*

"Tell me again," Ida said, turning to Earl, this pretty faced boy into whose hands she'd thrown her whole lot in life, "how we're gonna turn the Devil's Desert into God's Green Earth."

Earl walked over to the blue beard grass growing on the side of the dirt road they'd traveled miles beyond the Louisiana line. He reached down and pulled another tuft of the long blue blades out of the ground.

"Why it's just like what we just did with these here blades of grass, Ida," Earl said. "We took a piece of something worthless. Something stepped on every day by the poor saps coming and going from the burdensome business of life, and we turned it into something grand, like the paper says. Great and grand and glorious, just like Texas."

"Praise the Lord," Earl said, plucking the blades of beard grass one by one from the cluster and wiping them off on the belly of his shirt. "This here's gonna be our goldmine, Ida." He picked up an empty blue vile from the box next to Ida and threaded a new single blade of beard grass gently inside and popped the cork back on.

"Why, it's just like God's work, Ida," Earl said, holding the bottle before him. "We'll just feed the faithful in the promised land. And what's the harm in that?"

"Guess God ain't gonna smite us dead like I first thought he would," she laughed, and she pulled the farmer's dollar coin out of her pocket and plopped it into the rusted tobacco tin hidden beneath the bins of thimbles and boxes of nails.

"You know, giving that farmer that switch of dogwood, the one—what did you call it?—the one 'Dipped in the River Jordan by John the Baptist himself.' That was stroke of pure genius, Ida," Earl said. "And a real nice gesture, too, 'specially coming from a gal as sweet as you. We gotta keep that in," he muttered, looking deep into Ida's dark brown eyes.

Ida laughed and felt again a warmth sweep over her like the balm of the elixir, and suddenly she didn't regret any of it, not the leaving, nor the stealing, nor the trickery that was all they had to save themselves in the great wild land of Texas.

"Why thank you, Earl," she said. "I do think it was well worth that farmer's dollar."

Over Massanutten

Lee Scharf

Young Floyd was a wild child. Thin as a rail, smart as a whip, he was at the wheel of Darleen Smithhart's Bronco, she waiting tables at the Hungry House Café in Edenberg that night. Darleen let him drive her late Grandpa's old Bronco because it furthered along her Young Floyd, let's-get-married-sooner-than-later-agenda.

Darleen allowed as to how Young Floyd could take us over Massanutten Mountain to Fort Valley for the regular Friday night jam at the Fire House. The condition was that Young Floyd could borrow the Bronco if he and we, The Band, would fill up the tank after. And, we had to return it in the condition we found it, exactly. Darleen *always* had conditions. We said we'd all chip in and we'd bring back the Bronco exactly the way we found it, so Darleen said yes we could take it if just Young Floyd drove, but not you, Charlie.

"I got this, Darleen," Young Floyd said.

"You? Got it, Charlie, Charlie Remington? You got it?"

"Sure, sure, Young Floyd."

When I face the pearly gates, I just know I'll hear Ol' Saint Peter say, "Come on in, Charlie, Charlie Remington come on in," just like that. Never will figure it.

The whole town of Edenberg knows that Darleen Smithhart's Grandpa willed her the 1970s relic when he'd passed two months ago at the height of the fall color. Everyone was dumbfounded that he'd left it in mint running condition, with a new set of heavy tread tires, to fully utilize the four-wheel drive. Of course, you had to get out and click each hub by hand and then it growled like the devil when you geared it in, but so much the better according to Darleen. It was like her Grandpa Smithhart was sending her encouragement from the great Beyond when the Bronco made a noise like that.

Inside, the old Bronco was dirty as sin, years of grease, grime, and pipe smoke layered in. Jars of Folger's Coffee Crystals, rock hard Cremora in the glove compartment, coffee-stained plastic spoons, Tums.

After he died, Darleen found her Grandpa's bolo tie laid out 'cross the driver's seat, and she bawled like a baby when she saw it. Folks thought he'd put it there in preparation, because he'd decided he'd die on his birthday, surprise Grandma in heaven. He'd done it, too, died on his birthday, in his sleep, took care of all the details beforehand. A signature class act, dying on schedule like that.

They pumped his dead stomach empty of bananas and cream, likely his last supper since bananas and cream was his favorite dessert, bar none. No pills or powder evidence showed up, so it was ruled a natural death by Dr. Diehl, the coroner.

Young Floyd revved up the Bronco. John Milt and Porky, senior members of The Band, climbed in, they and their instruments. Porky in the front seat, John Milt beside me in the back, all of us without seat belts. Darleen had yet to remedy that act of Grandpa Smithhart's resistance to regulations. As uneasy as going without belts made us, we went for it anyway, in spite of it smelling like snow outside.

My gutbucket, safe in the Bronco's back-end, was tucked in with Grandpa Smithhart's WWII army blankets alongside Young Floyd's Dobro guitar, the Dobro itself a playable antique. I'd weathered my gutbucket outside for a season, using the shiny round tub to water the horses until the shine wore off of it. I'd found an old rake handle in the barn, bought some clothesline at Zerkel's Hardware, turned the bucket belly up, drilled a hole in its middle, strung the clothesline to its belly button, hammered a nail in the rake handle, braced the handle to the tub edge, good to go. Twang! All according to a Mother Earth News piece I'd googled at the Stoney Creek Library. The gutbucket fit right in with all the other antiques around town lately, counting the Bronco and the Dobro. Me and my gutbucket, we're the rhythm foundation to The Band. From my point of view, we're indispensable.

John Milton MacLeod carried his mandolin like a babe in his arms, and Porky Diehl, recently retired from the Fort Valley township police force, juggled his fiddle case between his knees in the front seat, moving it back and forth to balance the sway of the hairpin curves up and down the Edenburg Gap and on into Fort Valley.

I thought if Young Floyd'd been riding his buckskin mare, he'd be slapping her with the reins, sliding her around the hairpins on her haunches, whirling around those curves as we were.

When we headed down into Fort Valley, John Milt let loose with his song of the week:

Ida Bella, Ida Bella, Ida Bella!
I'm your fella, I'm your fella, I'm your fella!

Pick your tune. John Milt's bass rivaled Larry Hooper's of Oak Ridge Boys fame, meaning his voice was worth more than his lyrics. To prove the point, he hauled out his cell phone and played his Oak Ridge Boys' Elvira MP3 file as a sing along, to give Young Floyd and me a taste of the real thing and to show us proof positive that he was at least as good as Larry Hooper.

"Y'all hear about that dude out at Stroehdermann's who put that fussy saddle on an old nag backwards? And then rode her? And she let him?" Porky snorted.

"Yep. Must've been that mare, Old App. That Appaloosa's got the patience of a saint. She's seen it all," Young Floyd said.

"Lord, love us." John Milt could barely get the words out he was laughing so hard, tears streaming down his wrinkly cheeks and down his long, white pointy beard—we all were, just imagining, laughing so hard our sides hurt. Which is the first phase of what we did each and every Friday night—laugh our guts out to loosen up for the jam.

We hung a right into the Fire House parking lot, all the regulars pulling up in trucks mostly, bringing dishes to pass, since we always ate before we jammed. Porky pulled out his famous macaroni and cheese dish. John Milt, Justine's widower, brought her memorable French green bean and fried onion casserole, the shredded green beans glued together with Campbell's mushroom soup and crisped up with the fried onions he bought in a paper can at the Family Dollar. John Milt lines his shelves with mushroom soup and fried onions, says the cans are heat sinks, along with the pinto beans, and a comfort that keeps him close to Justine. Young Floyd, the designated driver, was off the hook for food. I brought the Coke. We could count on Raley to bring the rum lace.

"Hey, Young Floyd, where's Darleen? She let you drive her Bronco?" my sister, Sally Joy, yelled when we pulled into a parking spot. Meaning, what's in it for Darleen that she let you drive her inheritance?

Sally Joy was spiffed up in shades of hot pink. She believed hot pink was the color of love and dressed accordingly. Last year it was head to toe black that, while dramatic, had been off-putting. The tolerance of our parents is something to write home about. Tonight, Sally Joy's blinged, ears to feet and back. All for Young Floyd MacLeod, The Clueless.

My sister always has an edge to her voice where Darleen Smithhart's concerned. Catches in her craw that Young Floyd MacLeod and Darleen Smithhart are an item when everyone but Young Floyd knows he's straightaway in Sally Joy's heart.

Sally Joy and Darleen have a history that goes way back to their second grade playground days when Darleen was always a jump ahead of Sally Joy on the next second grade trend. During recess Sally Joy had had it when Darleen switched from Bring Your Dolls season to Jacks in the middle of the week and didn't tell Sally Joy. Sally Joy couldn't use her special little throw ball in the Jacks tournament that Darleen began without notice, just to get a leg up on Sally Joy. Sally Joy'd hauled off and hit Darleen in the jaw with a good upper left hook, Darleen'd grabbed one of Sally Joy's braids. Sally Joy clawed at Darleen's long strawberry blond hair, and they went at it off in a shady corner of the playground where Mrs. O'Malley, their favorite teacher, who'd had yard duty that day, couldn't see them.

Soon, Sally Joy knew that she was going to get beat. She pulled back, straightened her Brownie uniform and sash with the most badges in the second grade, and announced she shouldn't be fighting in uniform, and walked away. When she turned to look Darleen in the eye, Darleen smirked, and Sally Joy knew that Darleen knew that Sally Joy was beat. Fifteen years of dislike between those two, and still counting. And, now, Sally Joy was jealous of Darleen and Young Floyd with his black hair and blue eyes like the sky, but she'd die herself, maybe in her sleep for dramatic effect, before she'd admit it.

So, we ate, mellowed ourselves with rum and Coke, but not Young Floyd since he was driving, and Porky told the Stroehdermann joke, well-rehearsed as it was. We played pretty good, even though we played songs we all already knew backwards and forwards. No Crooked Still, No Old Crow Medicine Show, No Appalachian Hills, No New Grass. John Milt, in particular, wasn't one to break tradition with new stuff because it'd break the thread to the past that we of the Shenandoah Valley are charged with remembering.

"We live on sacred ground, Charlie. Listen to the music like that. Listen to the ground, Charlie, on a summer night when the fireflies are out and you can hear the dead soldiers in the ground, see their bones, Charlie, their bones. They're there. Can't dishonor that, now can you?"

For the life of me, I can't see that piecing together some new sounds would wipe out the past just like that. True, Young Floyd and I'd had the every-other-week warm-up routine to work from, but we needed more to stitch their bitching.

Porky and John Milt, ace musicians that they are, let it fly with the Orange Blossom Special. Porky's a fiddler to reckon with, a Valley gem. His Lorena'll make you cry like a baby. After the Orange Blossom Special my arm was ready for a rest, having kept up with Porky for the train rhythm of it, and Young Floyd's too, since Porky had us at lightning speed at the end, starting oh so slow, just to tease us with what was coming. Me and my gutbucket knew better than to slip in new rhythms with the Orange Blossom Special, so we didn't. At the end, John Milt was lightning speed itself; his mandolin wrist is as good as ever, which is worth mentioning since he's in his eighties.

Porky mopped his brow, took a swig, and when we all heard him start Lorena, the song that made the grey and the blue weep at night in their separate camps during the War of Northern Aggression right here in the Valley, getting some sleep so that they could kill each other the next day, either that or maybe just play checkers, gamble into eternity.

Sally Joy asked for a lift home, and we said well, yes, and she told her friend Emma and Emma said ok, then she would have room for Shelly whose husband had gone off to fight a fire in Conicville, being a volunteer fireman and all.

Young Floyd gunned up the Bronco's motor, geared it in low, turned right instead of left from the Fire House, geared up to third, joining half the people going down the Fort Valley Road, down being north because the River tells directions in the Valley, and it runs south to north. Maybe Young Floyd thought we didn't notice he was going in the wrong direction, but we did.

"What in God's name you up to, Young Floyd?" John Milt asked.

"You're not taking the Tower Road, now are you? You know the sign before Dead Man's Corner's latched up, road's closed for the season?"

"Maybe I do, maybe I don't. Maybe I forgot, being ADD and all, you think?"

"Not going to fly, Young Floyd," this from Porky.

I chimed in, "No way, José."

Sally Joy shifted her butt and tucked her skirt around her knees between John Milt and me, not saying a word.

"We're in four-wheel drive, did it earlier. No one notice the growl? Growled like Larry Hooper." Now he'd mentioned it, I had, but didn't think much about it.

"How you know we won't be skidding down on ice, Young Floyd?" I asked.

"What do you think, Charlie, Charlie Remington? What do you think? Rode my buckskin mare up from Leisure Point to check the dry, gravely spots this very morning. Rode her all the way to the Massadoah, gave her a drink, rode her back down, well, back up and then down. Piece of cake. We're doin' it, boys and Sally Joy."

Sally Joy looked thrilled to pieces that he had called her out, and she sent him a light beam smile of encouragement, Darleen eat your heart out written all over her face. Young Floyd saw it in the rearview mirror, and yelled, "Gee Haw!" That lit up smile was all Young Floyd needed. He turned up Woodstock Tower Road from the Fort Valley Road. Like it or not, John Milt, Porky, Sally Joy and I were along for the ride. Sally Joy, looking in the mirror at Young Floyd, begins to sing Driftwood Fire:

I grew up in the Appalachian Hills
I grew up in the Appalachian Hills
Swam at night in the Shenandoah
Rode my horse to the Massadoah
I grew up in the Appalachian Hills

Sally Joy could sing like Janis Joplin, maybe even better than Janis herself, I thought. A female Larry Hooper, but better, oh, so much better, grit and growl and *sweet*. Young Floyd joined in, his bass voice in harmony, making rhythm sounds like horses on a trail, as unlikely as you might think it. The two of them together just took your breath away, even if she is my sister. Darleen was losing ground and no mistake.

We passed Fort Valley Elementary, got our first hint of ice on the road, but Young Floyd found some bare sandy patches and pulled us on up the mountain. We passed the gap that takes you over to the Massadoah. Sally Joy and Young Floyd never missed a beat.

Hair-pinning up Massanutten Mountain to the Woodstock Tower's one thing, coming down's an entirely different kettle of fish. At the Tower, we got out to whizz in the woods, our habit after a jam since a few years back. Sally Joy figured what we were up to, living with four brothers as she does. No one said a word, but not because of Sally Joy. We'd scared ourselves speechless, except for Young Floyd who started whistling Heart of my Heart, when friends were dearer then.

Young Floyd headed us down the mountain, starting off real slow, not using the brakes, just easing the Bronco, one side to the other. The Bronco's engine held us back a bit. Darleen's Grandpa'd switched the engine at 200,000 miles, thinking ahead of Darleen, I'm sure.

We knew this road like the back of our hands, having ridden it so much, but never like this. We ground our way down in low four-wheel drive with the Bronco holding on well enough, Young Floyd the Fearless steering it out of a few slides, talking to the old Ford like it was a filly.

"Come on, Sweetheart, hold the muddy ruts, nice and easy. Here's some gravel for you. There you go, Baby."

I thought, Young Floyd's feeling something in his hands the way they're on the wheel. He's riding the small bumps of the frozen ruts like an artist laying down a line. Sally Joy had her eyes shut, probably imagining Young Floyd talking bedroom talk to her. Geeze Leweeze, I would prefer not to think those thoughts about my sister. Maybe I'm a pervert.

We all knew we were coming to the Hairpin of all Hairpins, where the drop off on the left side of the Bronco went a hundred feet straight down. In the summertime, we'd joke it off, get all scared, but never had a doubt. Not tonight. We were lit up by a half moon, and I guess that helped, but when we started to slide to the far wrong edge, I knew we were goners.

To his credit, Young Floyd never lost it, nor did his ADD kick in, maybe tamped down because of an adrenalin rush, praise the Lord for small favors. Jesus, please help us, Young Floyd had his eyes on the road, breathing slow and easy, humming some kind of damned off tune, Good Lord, and we all knew he held no fear because we held it all between the four of us.

In a cool, calm voice Young Floyd says,

"Okay, okay all of you in the back, move real slow, move real slow, slide real smooth-like up the hill in your seat there. Just glide yourselves up toward Charlie's door. Gooood. We're gonna shift the weight of this here bronc up the hill, up the hill. Smooth as a baby's behind, that's it, that's it. Roll down your window real slow, Charlie, Charlie Remington hang yourself over the door. You, too, Sally Joy, you sweet thing."

Sally Joy's eyes were as big as blue peerie marble shooters on a playground. John Milt shored her up from the front seat and over the door, she hanging half way out the Bronco, just like me, then John Milt slid himself up, moving from the front to brace the both of us with all of his four feet ten. Porky did his part, too, and his butterball weight hanging over the door made all the difference. We felt the Bronco shift just a bit toward the upper bank, away from the hundred foot drop on this part of the Tower Road that is no more than a two-way horse trail. Sally Joy let out a trembly sigh.

Next we felt the old Bronco slip down the hill, then stop, then slip again, going slow enough even if we were bent at a crazy angle, hanging over the door like rag dolls with a gut ache. I tried to think all of us up the slant, and didn't let myself laugh, but I felt crazy funny. Well, maybe I'll die laughing, I thought. Not so bad. I felt Sally Joy's tears drop on my arm, and I sobered up.

Young Floyd, still calm as heck, says, "I'm gonna steer the Bronco real careful up against the tree just down a little ways, up against the hill, y'all know the big white oak I'm talking about here, the one's roots come out the road?" We did. "When we catch into the tree and our tires are in between her roots, I want y'all to get out, real careful, mind. If we get so much as a scratch on Darleen's Grandpa's Bronco here, I'm a dead man."

Well, we caught ourselves into the arms of the white oak and bumped ourselves into her road roots. We crawled out through the open window of the Bronco, falling on our faces into the dark wet dirt and twigs, and I, being six feet and more, caught my feet on the doorframe. Maybe I was thinking I could keep the Bronco from falling over the edge of the mountain by holding on with my toes. God only knows.

Damned if Porky didn't bring his fiddle with him, and John Milt his mandolin. I loosed my toes one foot at a time and left the Bronco and Young Floyd to their fate. They held, thank the Good Lord God Almighty.

Sally Joy was hiccupping sobs, trying not to wail, probably consumed with Young Floyd hero worship while trying to play his heroine lover in her ever-active mind, or maybe she was just plumb terrified. Well, Young Floyd deserved some hero worship, but he damn well had been a fool to think that we wouldn't get iced over when the sun set, at least here and there, and we were all fools for going along with him. To give him his due, he'd landed the old Bronc next to the tree, bumper first, without a scratch.

"Charlie, Charlie Remington, you know where the ropes are in the back of the Bronco?" I did, just to the right of my gutbucket, up against the tire well in a greasy gunnysack.

"Open the back door. Bring 'em out, one by one. Gentle now, Boy." He was talking to me like I was a gol-durned colt.

With the touch of a true master, I opened the side-hinged back door of the Bronco, gentle beyond gentle-like, undid the gunny sack, handed a piece of rope to Porky, who handed it on to John Milt who pulled it out full length. Then, the other one. The ropes pulled out nice and easy, coiled as they'd been by Darleen's Grandpa himself, craftsman that he was. I clicked back the door one notch, slow, easy, click.

We tied the ropes to the front bumper tie loop on the driver's side, then to a sapling up road, and all three of us pulled on the Bronco's chassis away from the white oak while Young Floyd cut the tires hard into the hill and then left, letting the Bronco slide down, free of the tree and its bare roots. Praise God, he found a patch of bare gravel and we were back in business.

Steady as we were on a patch of gravel, Young Floyd whooped, "Everybody in!" We coiled the ropes, threw them into the back of the Bronco, asking Darleen's Grandpa's forgiveness for not coiling just right. I heard the ropes thump my gutbucket, making jumpy rhythms when they fell, no matter, better the gutbucket than the Dobro.

We piled in, Young Floyd straightened the wheels and we were off, but no more Giddy Up. No more singing, no more talking, just Sally Joy's raggedy breaths.

We made it down the rest of the hill, except for a little sliding just past Leisure Point coming into Rivermont at the Burnshire Bridge. By then, we were yahooing and slapping our knees, praising Young Floyd to the heavens, ignoring the fact that he'd taken us to death's door in the first place.

Young Floyd kept looking into the rearview mirror and smiling at Sally Joy. Heaven wouldn't be a match for Sally Joy's joy tonight, me thinking Heaven was where she would end up some day, but not tonight.

Our victory dance in place didn't last long. When we turned left to cross the Burnshire Bridge, we heard the sirens, saw the Fort Valley squad car *and* the Virginia State Police car speed up to chase us down, the state police car in the lead. Porky looked pale as a ghost; he could expect no mercy from his former police force buddies who had beat us to the Burnshire Bridge by taking the Edenberg Gap, the Valley Pike, and Mill Road in record time. Porky would never hear the end of it. Wondering if his firehouse fiddling reputation would survive the night was written all over his face. He hugged his fiddle. How could he ever play Lorena for the tears, when everyone's tears were really a big laugh out? John Milt groaned and turned his tam round in his hands.

Sally Joy looked like a deer in the headlights. I forgot to breathe.

Young Floyd, after all he had done up there on the mountain and down, hit the gas. We crossed the bridge at lightning speed, no ice, turned right, headed west for Woodstock to Mill Road, the law on our tail. We were well on our way to passing the open cornfields when the winds blew in, dumping snow, a whiteout.

Way before Dead Man's Corner we hit a stretch of ice when the wind petered out. The squad cars and the Bronc hit the ice at the same time. All three cars swerved on all fours making 360s first one way then another when we steered ourselves out of our crazy spins, or tried to.

In the quiet of the night, we rolled ourselves to a standstill. All of us sputtered to a stop, engines still on the go. I smelled burnt rubber. Young Floyd stopped within inches of the state patrol car, head on. We criminals were stranded in the dark of night.

The Fort Valley squad car righted itself directly behind the state patrol car, held to like a duck following its Mama, except Fort Valley kept spinning its wheels in place. Everyone and their brother, except Sally Joy, swore a blue streak.

First the state patrol car, and then Fort Valley switched off their engines. Young Floyd killed the Bronco. Silence, except we could hear the Shenandoah spill over the dam, going down north.

"What in tarnation were y'all thinking, coming down the Tower Road when the sign was flipped up? Tower Road's closed! Y'all could've been killed. Should've been. You know full well we're going to have to charge you. What in blazes we going to charge them with, Donnie?" Fort Valley police officer Zirkle looked to Virginia Highway Patrolman Patton for an answer.

Porky, showing his mettle, the fine, creative law enforcement officer that we all loved and respected, though retired, said, "Well, y'all know that they never did get around to replacing that flipped up sign coming up the Tower Road from the Fort that the snowplow plowed under a few weeks back. Maybe we didn't know we shouldn't have attempted the attempt."

We all looked at each other, eyebrows raised, seeing a way out, thank you, Porky.

"Now, we *were* driving without seat belts. Darleen hasn't gotten around to it, you know. You could charge us and her with a seat belt violation, if you want to do some bean countin' for your time, which you do," Porky went on, savvy as he was and still is.

Young Floyd looked at Sally Joy, horrified, thinking of what Darleen would say to being ticketed. Sally Joy looked at Young Floyd with misty-eyed fake sympathy. The rest of us began to laugh, tears rolling down our cheeks, our sides and guts splitting for the second time that night. To their credit, Maxie Zirkle and Donnie Patton joined in; after all, we're all Valley boys, even Sally Joy some days.

We Valley boys, Sally Joy included, went into the woods, pulled pine boughs to put in the icy ruts. We got past the cornfield snow patch to Dead Man's Corner by fits and starts, riding the pine boughs over the ice, getting out to pave the way with pine boughs again and again 'til we came close to Dead Man's Corner where the road angles to the left then right up and around. The state car and Fort Valley slowed down when we made a run shot up and around the Corner, hung a right to the dry and the safe, then they made their run shots and we all of us were on dry pavement, in the clear to be ticketed for seat belt violations.

Officers Zirkle and Patton pulled us over like regular. They probably noted the time of night and our coordinates on their GPS trackers. We obliged, and we and Darleen got charged, entered into the databases. Young Floyd was given two piles of paper tickets, one set from Patton, the other from Zirkle, thanks to Porky's negotiation skills. Young Floyd the Fearless looked as pale as Porky had looked when Zirkle and Patton began the chase in the first place. Young Floyd knew that Darleen would rake him twice over for two tickets. He'd offer to pay the difference on her insurance if that would turn down the boil. Young Floyd the Fearless feared his sweetheart, Darleen; I Charlie Remington, loved her spunk.

Maxie and Donnie went their separate ways. Young Floyd, Porky, John Milt and I rotated the Bronco's hubs back to 2WD, each one got one, Porky singing call me mellow fellow, marching to his own drum. Young Floyd started up the Bronco, took one last look in the mirror to catch Sally Joy's eye, headed us all back to the Hungry House Café and Darleen, Young Floyd going so slow we had to tell him to get a move on to drive the speed limit.

Young Floyd slowed down the Bronco, came to a stop at the flipped-up sign that said Tower Road was closed and reached out to unlatch it so it would say Tower Road was open. I said, real quiet, "Don't, Young Floyd, just don't." He looked at me in the rearview mirror, turned to look at Sally Joy full on.

Sally Joy gave Young Floyd one sultry smile and began to sing sweet as an angel, not at all like Janis, never unlocking her eyes from Young Floyd's, putting a little extra into the line, "how sweet thou art."

Ah, the tables at the Hungry House Café are beginning to turn, Darleen, my sweet, the tables are beginning to turn.

A Perfect Heart Shot

George Drew

One squirrel was black, the other gray. The black was young and the sheen of its fur uncompromised by defect. The gray was aging. Its fur was dull and seeded white. But it was as agile as the black in sport. Up and down the elm they flashed, around and around its trunk, their claws snagging bark and creeper vine. They chirred and growled.

Polly was careful not to move. He was seated on a log just off the spur road, halfway between the levee and the river. It was a good spot. He could see the entire scope of woods, which extended at its widest point no more than two hundred yards from levee to river. Keeping still was easy. Though the log was decayed at both ends, the middle was solid enough and shod of bark. On it he was comfortable, alert. And it was warm for a late November day—though not excessively. Chain smoking kept off the mosquitoes. Plus there was much to occupy him. Like the squirrels. Or the birds, the kind Old Man Cook called half-breeds. It was even possible he might spot some turkeys. He had seen a hoot owl. It was quiet and there was no wind. So he could hear things, too. A fine drizzle added to the effect by dampening everything. Underfoot the leaves were a brown slush.

Polly raised his Remington very slowly. Through the Weaver 'scope he sighted in on the black squirrel. "Boom!" he whispered. "Gotcha!" Of course, he didn't really shoot. It was just pretend. He knew what an ought-six shell would do to a squirrel. Besides, he didn't want to ruin his stand. He was after buck.

He lowered his rifle. As he did so, off to his right something caught his eye. Careful not to move too suddenly, he turned his head and looked down the spur road toward the levee. Not more than fifteen yards away stood the most magnificent buck he'd ever seen. It was a six-point, the rack flaring like misplaced wings. Twin streams of breath rushed from its nostrils. Its flag was at half-mast, alert but not alarmed. It was big and strong.

Polly knew he was going to miss. It wasn't a premonition exactly. After nine years of misses, both close and otherwise, he had come to expect them. To connect now, in the first few minutes of the first day of the season, would be at odds with likelihood. This buck was too grand for such an easy kill.

And he had the fever. He felt the familiar rush of blood, the heart starting its heaving thud. His hands were sweaty, and they shook. He was breathing fast and his eyes refused to clear. Blinking hard, he fit the Remington snugly to his shoulder and placed his cheek flush against the stock. He positioned the crosshairs slightly off center on the buck's neck. Then he held his breath.

The sound was deafening. It rolled off across the levee like a tidal wave and exploded against the Delta sky. The squirrels vanished, and the birds. Where the buck had got to Polly couldn't say. All he was aware of was decibels and kick, to which he had reacted by half-closing his eyes. It was just long enough. When he looked again, the buck was gone.

Donnie Mondale appeared. He was the other cutoff man and had been positioned about fifty yards closer to the river.

"Did you get him?"

"Nah."

Just then Richard and the Cook boys—Leroy and Jimmi Carl—stepped from the woods into the road. They had been the drivers.

"Who shot?"

"Me."

"Did you git 'im?"

"Nah."

Richard crooked his rifle in an arm and leaned against a tree. That he was Polly's brother was obvious. Though at five-ten he was taller and more built, he had the same plumply rugged face and the same web of curly hair—his black and Polly's brown, matching their different complexions. What was really different were the eyes. Polly's were hazel and soft, his a fierce green. They and his mouth always signaled his intentions. Right now, they were narrowed and unblinking, his mouth harmonizing with a hard half-smile.

"What happened, Polly-boy?" he teased.

"Missed."

"Whooee!" Leroy squalled and did a little jig. "Hey, boy, did you say you *missed?*"

Polly smiled. Leroy's teasing he didn't mind. That was just his way. He was a large man, topping out at around two-fifty, and was good-natured in a way that made people feel comfortable, even when the butt of a joke. He was red-faced, was balding slightly and his eyes sparkled with humor and affability. It was apparent he was content with himself and his lot.

"No chance for another shot?" Jimmi Carl said.

"Yeah, but my gun got hung up," Polly explained. He was apt to be more long-winded with Jimmi Carl. Unlike Leroy, Jimmi Carl never played the fool. Even though he, too, was a large man, perhaps twenty pounds lighter than Leroy and of a pleasant enough disposition, he was more serious and didn't clown so much. His humor was more subtle and less raucous. Polly thought it must be because he didn't have a big belly like Leroy's.

"Guess we'd best take a look at the action on that deer-zinger before we come out in the mornin'," Jimmi Carl advised. "Maybe you'll git another crack at 'im."

Polly nodded. "And I won't miss next time," he vowed.

"A promise ain't a git, Polly-boy," Richard mocked.

Polly glared. That not only angered, it stung. Could he help it if he had no luck? Bad luck had been the rule for nine deer seasons. Like the last one: He had shot four times at a buck as it ran across the levee. Wide open—and he had missed every shot. The fever again. He still hadn't lived that down. And naturally,

Richard had ridden him about it every chance he'd got. Polly had vowed the tenth season would be different. So far it hadn't.

And he could be sure his brother would remind him. Normally, Richard, who was a good and successful hunter, was totally indifferent to Polly's lack of success. Indifferent to Polly, period. But not during deer season. He was unmerciful then. Later Polly told Donnie Richard was a jinx.

So it was Richard's fault he'd missed. And when he missed the second time, he said it was because he'd had the fever big time. But he lied. It was the other way around. The fever had him.

The next morning was like the one before. It was drizzling and muggy, with patches of ground fog spiraling across the open grazing land bordering the levee.

At five the rite began. First was the coming together. This they accomplished separately, arriving one after the other at the Cooks': Richard, primed as always, then Polly, then Donnie, late as always.

Next came the coffee and the talk. They gathered in the dining room, fanning outward in a half-circle from the space heater. Old man Cook, arthritic and always cold, sat not more than five feet from the heater, which he kept turned up high. From there, he would guide them through a maze of recollection: old hunts, old cohorts, old adventures.

"Why, boys, I recall it was back in nineteen-n-thirty I got my first buck—a big critter..."

And so it went. They would listen, sipping their coffee and stretching into wakefulness, until the talk, like the coffee, began to cool. That was the signal.

"Looks like it's gittin' light out," Jimmi Carl observed. He smiled at Polly. "We'd best git up and went, so's Polly here can git another crack at that six-point."

Leroy stood up and did his morning jig. "Whooee!" he said. "Remember now, boy, you only supposed to need *one* shot."

Everyone laughed except Donnie. Quiet as always, he was sitting in a red kitchen chair and busily scratching his legs.

"What's wrong, Donnie?" said Leroy, knowing full well what was wrong. "Got the itchies this mornin'?"

"Yeah," Donnie admitted, "Those damn cactus vines nearly ate me up yesterday."

Leroy smiled pornographically. "Or *something*," he said.

Richard's green eyes started jumping. "Yeah," he said, motioning toward Polly, "and maybe that's what happened to *him*—cactus vine of the finger. Right, Polly-boy?"

Polly ignored him. "Anybody got a red hat I can use?" he said. "I forgot mine."

"I have one," Richard purred. "You're welcome to it, boy."

Polly wondered what he wanted.

And last, the hunt. It began with the drive five miles south to Frear's Tuck. Polly liked this part very much. There was no talk to speak of as they bounced in Jimmi Carl's pickup along the dirt and gravel road that topped the levee. But there was the thick scent of anticipation. Together they would spill blood. And spilling blood tied them together.

Light was just unveiling trees and grass as they arrived. They would begin the drive in the same place as on the day before—a spur road about one mile north of the game preserve. Another road marked that boundary. There two men would sit cutoff, about fifty yards apart. The other three would line up abreast of each other at about thirty-yard intervals and make the drive. Any deer in the narrow scope of woods should go right to the men on stand.

"Polly, you sit cutoff again," Jimmi Carl said. "So's you can git another shot at your buck."

But Polly refused. "No, you. It's your turn today, Jimmi Carl. You and Donnie."

"But it's Leroy's turn, too," Donnie objected.

"No, you go," Leroy said. "I'd just as soon walk—might git me a gobbler that way."

"Okay, Polly," Jimmi Carl said, "but drivin' you might not even git a look at 'im."

Polly shrugged. Fair was fair. "Maybe he'll double back," he said.

Jimmi Carl and Donnie drove off. The three drivers lined up along the spur road, Polly nearest the river, to his left Richard, then Leroy. They were quiet now, anticipating. The first quarter-mile or so would be easy going—mostly open stands of oak and elm. After that it would get rough, especially for Polly. Along the river's bank were long stretches of thick briars and low-growing shrubs, the kind of places deer loved. Until then, he and Richard would be mostly in sight of each other and could talk and imitate hounds to move the deer. Once in that briar- and shrub-infested terrain, however, there would be no breath for talking or howling. Leroy's lot was easier. Closer to the levee, trees dominated, with only occasional patches of heavy grass and briars. He could stroll all the way.

They allowed Jimmi Carl and Donnie ten minutes to get set. Then they began the drive.

It had stopped raining, but everything was wet. Ten feet off the spur road and Polly's cotton trousers were soaked. Still-hunting would be good on such a day. But the object of driving was to make a lot of noise. That would be difficult when the underbrush and leaves were mush underfoot. And wet limbs wouldn't scrape and snap so readily. It was just too quiet. Leroy and Richard thought so too. No sooner had they stepped off the road than they began howling. Polly didn't think they needed his help, so he kept silent.

Twenty yards in from the road the grass and weeds gave way to woods. As he walked, Polly scanned the undergrowth for deer and the ground for sign. Occasionally he would adjust his pace to keep abreast of Richard and Leroy, who bobbed in and out of sight. In the heavier growth ahead he would look for Richard's red hat.

There was abundant sign. Deer trails went in every direction, angling eventually toward the river. It was soon evident why. Ten minutes of walking had brought Polly to where the woods veered toward the levee around the stretch of open terrain bordering closely on the river. It was a good half-mile to where the woods turned back. Before him was an obstacle course of briars, tall grass and tough, vine-like shrubs. In spots they reached to his chest.

Straight ahead was the only way. The scope of woods and land had narrowed considerably, and Polly could hear Richard moving just inside the woods, though he could see him only occasionally—hat flitting like a red bird between trees and from behind shrubs.

On the Arkansas side of the river there was a salvo. Polly counted four shots. Tough deer or lousy shot. Then, more excitingly, two ahead. Could it have been Jimmi Carl? Or Donnie? It sounded farther off than that.

Polly lunged ahead. Immediately, briars snagged at his legs and shrubs, his hips and upper body. At one point he was so tangled he couldn't move. To free himself he slammed his body hard against the shrubs and used the stock of his rifle as a club. When a rabbit kicked up right under his feet he was glad he wasn't hunting them. He couldn't even get the rifle to his shoulder.

Every step was a battle. Polly was fatigued before he'd gone a quarter-mile. Worse, he was beginning not to care, and that was bad. So he stopped for a breather. Though he couldn't see Richard, he could hear the indistinct mumble of his and Leroy's voices. They were more than thirty yards inside the woods. Evidently, Richard had angled toward the levee. Polly wondered what they were talking about. He guessed they were resting, too.

On the river a skiff chugged by. In it were three hunters. One waved at Polly. He stood and waved back. Then he moved ahead again, fighting the vegetation for another hundred yards. At last he gave out. He decided he would move closer in, toward the woods. Of course, it probably would mean some missed deer. But he guessed they'd be there another day.

He turned left. At the edge of the open area, not ten feet

from the woods, he saw a clump of locust trees. That would be a good place to come out.

But he'd gone no more than halfway when he stopped. He'd heard a noise just south of the locust trees. He tried to see, but there were tall shrubs obscuring his view. He moved left about five feet.

Then he saw it. Coming through the grass and shrubs as if they weren't there was his deer. He was sure it was the same. There was no mistaking that rack. The buck had its head low to the ground, its tail turned down so no white showed. It was placing each hoof carefully, sneaking between him and Richard.

Polly was calm this time. His heart was normal, eyes clear, breath steady. Carefully he picked his shot, measuring the distance and checking for obstructions. The buck had stopped just to the right of one of the locust trees. It was in no hurry. Neither was he.

The buck moved forward a few steps. Now it was in front of the tree. At the edge of the woods, directly in back, there was a flash of red.

Polly raised his rifle. As the clap of thunder rolled once, twice, three times across the river and bounced against the levee, the buck leapt straight up, all four legs clearing the ground, twisted to its right, and nosedived back to earth, its hindlegs thrashing wildly into shudders.

Polly was confused. He had heard the noise, he had smelled the acrid gunpowder, and he had seen the buck do its death dance. But he had felt no recoil, had seen no spurt of flame. Then he realized he hadn't shot.

It was Richard who got to the body first, then Leroy. Richard said it was a perfect heart shot. "It surely was," Leroy chimed in, admiringly. Richard also said he hadn't seen Polly, only the buck. And besides, he added, better *someone* bagged it rather than its getting off scot-free.

"You gotta be quicker on the draw, Polly-boy," advised Richard in his most serious voice.

Polly said nothing.

The Jungle

Hillary Behrman

It is still dark out when Corky picks up Miles at the group home. Corky believes in being punctual. It shows she has her shit together. Besides, as his social worker, she likes to model desired behavior. The traffic, usually such a bitch on I-5, isn't as bad as she expected. They arrive early for the court hearing and sit in her car in the underground parking garage across the street from the courthouse. She'd been too stressed about the traffic to make a stop at the McDonald's drive thru. It doesn't matter. She keeps a tote bag full of packaged snacks in the back seat, and she reaches back, grabs the bag, and swings it into Miles' lap. She watches him rifle through the contents, ferreting out a green foil-wrapped granola bar and a ridiculously small box of raisins. Ridiculous, that's what she is. There couldn't be more than four or five shriveled little rabbit turds in the thing. God knows why she buys them. She lets Miles fiddle with the radio, but the reception sucks.

They watch the parking stalls fill up. They watch the judge as she parks her silvery car with the doors that *beep beep* when she walks away without her having to do a damn thing. They listen to her low elegant heals *click click* against the cement as she walks to the bank of elevators. The judge is looking at her phone, doesn't even see them. Miles starts to get out of the car.

"Wait." Corky places her hand on his shoulder, holding him back, pinning him to the seat. Too intimate, not what she intends at all. He looks his question at her, *what?*

"Awkward."

That is all the explanation she is prepared to give as her hand, the one that held him back, floats into the air and waves toward the disappearing back of the judge. They wait some more. Both of them staring straight through the windshield at the concrete wall in front of them. It is cracked, the crack is beaded with water, sweating.

In the courtroom, the judge signs the papers that officially take Miles away from Missy for the last time. He can't be given back. "The right outcome for all concerned." The judge is looking at the papers when she says this, so Miles doesn't know who she is talking to until she looks up and gives a nod at the adults who stand on either side of him behind the long wooden table. Miles looks down. The surface of the table is polished. He looks at the grown-ups foreshortened bodies, watches their wavy distorted faces reflect back up at him. Missy's face isn't there. Miles thinks about the word *concerned* so he doesn't have to think about Missy. He's never heard the word used that way. He thought *concern* was a feeling, a mash up of fear and wanting, what he's always felt for Missy. His eyes feel gritty like he forgot to wash away the bits of sleep from their corners. If tears are there, they'll never make it through all the gunk.

After court, Corky walks Miles to the bus stop and asks if he wants bus tokens or a ride back up the hill to school? He takes the tokens.

She says, "It's over Miles." She shakes her head back and forth, disgusted with herself. "That's not what I meant. It's not over. I just meant no more court hearings. That's what I should have said."

She gives him a hug and he lets her. He's been through years of other people's houses and monthly trips to court. The last time Missy was at court she wouldn't tell anyone where she was living. But Miles is not a kid anymore. He's thirteen, the same age Missy was when she had him. He will find her.

Miles waits for the #3 bus at the corner of Third and James until Corky is out of sight. Downtown smells like piss, not just the alley behind him, the whole place. When they knocked down the viaduct and started digging the tunnel under the Sound there were fissures. Water bubbled up from the deep, warping the sidewalk in front of the courthouse. But Miles thinks the problem is above ground, rivers of urine, some of it his own, sinking into the pavement. The city must have reached a tipping point, saturation. There is nowhere else for it to go. They are wading around in their own waste. It's like the public swimming pool up on 23rd where he goes after school. Every kid pretends they never pee in the pool, they just put their heads down and swim through the warm spots. When he was little, Missy would say, "That's how life is baby—full of piss." She'd taught him to swim. She had made sure he wore rubber boots.

The case file is how Miles found out where his mother is living. Sometimes he crashes in Corky's office after school when he's between one placement and the next. Corky keeps a sleeping bag and pillow under her desk and lets him roll it out in the corner while she makes phone calls. She must have figured he was too wiped out or strung out for her to worry about putting away the file. But when she goes for coffee he makes his way through the log notes, page after page working backward through his own life. *Mother: system raised, homeless.* Three words after mother with a colon. Miles thinks it should be a semi-colon, but he doesn't really know. He read the page again and again, *system raised*, sounded like a chicken bred for slaughter. *Father unknown.* In the margin, next to *place of residence*, Corky has scribbled, *The Jungle.*

The Jungle. A place carved out of the steep embankments at the base of Beacon Hill and underneath the freeways where I-5 and I-90 get all tangled up in express lanes and exit ramps. The viaducts crisscross back and forth, forming a canopy of metal I-beams and reinforced concrete, shielding the cars passing overhead from the people camping below.

Miles looks for Missy there. It's a leaky afternoon between court-ordered visits. He's been keeping his backpack stuffed with offerings for her. He has KitKats, a Moon Pie, a half-pint of chocolate milk and a square plastic-foil covered bowl of Cocoa Puffs he took from the school cafeteria. She likes chocolate. They both do. He catches the first bus after the last school bell. He's done the calculations. If he keeps moving, he can make it there, find her, and make it back to his foster placement before he's even missed.

He boards the bus from the front, swipes his pass, heads to the back. The bus is half empty, but he doesn't sit down. He hovers near the rear door, counting the city blocks with taps of his hand on the sticky metal bar that runs across the back of an empty row of seats. His body sways as he pulls the cord early so the rear door folds open before the bus comes to a complete stop. Bus and boy working together, *sweet symbiosis*, that's what he thinks as he bursts out the door, clears the steps and hits the pavement with both feet. His body moves down Dearborn at full speed, leaping Parkour style over cement barriers. He sprints across the highway, zigzagging around rows of gargantuan grey cement columns. He's in the Jungle. He's pumped.

Today it will be different, he can feel it. Everything is in motion, not just him. The universe is working with him to help him find her. The cars above him sound like thunder. They shake the dirt under his feet and for a moment he wobbles, drops to a crouch like they taught in elementary school. Earthquake. He knows he's being stupid. He stands back up and shakes his arms and legs, limbering up like someone getting ready to fight. He starts to move again, but not as fast as he did out in the open. He is looking this way and that. A person has to pay attention down here. If you don't look hard, you don't see. Only with close inspection does the place begin to reveal it is thickly settled. It doesn't take long before he finds her.

Her camp is tidy. The dirt is swept into swirling grooves in front of a tan REI dome tent with a blue tarp rigged up to provide an extra layer of protection from the wet and debris that rains down from the highway.

"What are you doing here, Miles?"

"Nothing, just checking it out…"

"What, you came to look at me like a fucking monkey in the zoo?"

"No Ma, I just, I just wanted to see you."

"Well, you seen me, now get out of here."

"Here." He shoves a candy bar at her. She shoves it back.

"You keep it, baby. You look too skinny."

"So do you."

Missy pulls the zipper up higher on her hoodie. They stand facing each other. Memorizing and comparing like they do each time they meet. His skin is pale and freckled like hers, but his nose is broad, his lips full. His hair is red like hers, but in tight curls clipped close to his skull. Both sets of eyes are flecked brown and green and hooded in a way that makes people think they aren't paying attention.

She loses herself in watching him. She feels something close to joy when he turns away and she catches a glimpse of the place where his hair forms a razor-neat border between the base of his head and the tendon thickening his neck.

"Really, baby, you can't be here."

They both know it. But he is here. They feel something shift, a new weight to be balanced between them. A change in the wind carries the acrid smell of burning rubber.

"Go."

There is something in her voice. And for the first time since he entered the Jungle he is scared.

"I said, Go!"

So he does.

He runs. He's still clutching the candy bars, one in each hand. Only when he is out of her sight does he stop. He unwraps the KitKats, and snapping both chocolate bars into twigs, he shoves all the sticks into his mouth at once. He stands there chewing and chewing. When he is finally done, he walks away. He does not run under the green steel arches of the Jose Rizal

149

Bridge and out toward downtown. No. Instead, he follows one of the dirt paths up through another cluster of tents and into the park next to the bridge.

The park is carefully tended, the grass clipped, edged, and speckled with small white flowers. Rabbits are everywhere, nibbling. Miles makes his way back along this greenbelt that stretches its skin taut over I-90. He sees a small brown bunny being pecked to death by a crow. He chases the crow off, but the animal's intestines are spooled out in a hot pink whorled tube that can't be shoved back in. The creature's eyes are wide open, alert and shining. Its white chest rises and falls. Miles has no way to kill it. He wanders away, searching for a rock or big stick. Relieved when he returns, rock in hand, to find that the rabbit's eyes are glazed over, the ribcage stilled.

After Miles is gone Missy can't bear that she sent him away. But she couldn't stand it either, his being here, looking at her.

When Missy was much younger than Miles is now and still living rough with her dad, he liked to leave the city, hitch out to the mountains with his big metal framed backpack and Missy in tow. Missy only now wonders if that was how he kept Children's Services off his back for as long as he did. He was always in search of the perfect campsite, a place of their own. He would drag her up one ridge and across another, down heather-rimmed game trails to find the perfect rock outcropping. He would order Missy to spin in a circle, "Keep your eyes wide open girl." She made sure she could see mountains all the way around. That was where they would pitch their tent.

When Miles was little and still with Missy, she liked to play the same game with him here in the city. She was partial to the small green islands of urban wilderness nestled between sections of freeway—buffeted on both sides by fast-moving cars. The sound was muffled but still loud. There was always a stiff wind in these places like when an updraft cuts through a canyon.

When Missy got pregnant, she had asked Corky to take her to get an abortion. There are no notes about this in the case file. Corky made the appointment and used her own car to drive Missy to the clinic, which was in a small strip mall near the airport, its entrance jammed in between Big 5 Sporting Goods and Payless Shoes. The Doctor's hands were big, and his skin was grey and looked dirty even though Missy and Corky watched him scrub repeatedly at the sink. He tried to reassure them by saying, "It's nothing, a clump of cells, gone in a moment, better off without it." But his hands shook, and his breath smelled like re-heated fried chicken. Missy sat up, twisting her feet out of the stirrups, paper gown riding up on her skinny bare hips. She'd barely got the words out, "I can't be here." before Corky was stretching out her hand, helping her down, handing over her jeans, yellow cotton underpants nestled inside.

It had rained while they were inside the clinic, and warm mist rose from the pavement. Corky and Missy sat in the blue Saturn. The windows steamed up. Tears dripped down both their faces. A full-grown-woman and scrawny girl struck dumb by their shared understanding of how inevitable walking out of that room had been.

As Corky turned the key in the ignition and eased her foot off the brake, her mind spooled back over the years, cataloging each placement, each time she had failed the girl sitting beside her. But she couldn't apologize, what was the point? Missy had expected no better.

As they pulled out onto the street, Missy rolled down her window and stuck her face out into the damp wind tunnel of air rushing between the cars. She believed, like her father, that a clean stiff wind could make all the difference.

And for a while it did.

Each time they took Miles away from Missy, there were a couple of days when all Missy felt was relief. She'd sleep all night and into the next day. When she was finally fully awake, she would realize she couldn't feel a thing, not one damn thing, inside or out. Nothing, not one sensation good or bad no matter how hard she pinched and scraped at herself. It was as if there were no nerve endings anywhere on her body. It was as if her skin only registered touch when it was coming from his mouth, his cheek, and his small sticky fingers.

So she had run. Hoping the wind, the rain, the cold, anything would trigger a sensation. There were bits of broken glass, dirt and sticks rubbing back and forth into the exposed skin of her back as the guy on top of her moved up and down. Still she felt nothing. So she pulled her shit together. Because what was the point of anything if she never got to feel Miles' wet, sleepy breath against her skin again?

She decides she'd stop at the day hygiene center, shower and put on her visiting clothes. She kept a clean pair of jeans, a pale pink t-shirt, and a yellow flowered cardigan rolled in a five-gallon Ziploc freezer bag at the bottom of her knapsack. She had enough of her own money to buy Miles a chocolate Frosty and a small fries. *Jesus now he's stealing goddamn Moon Pies for her.*

When he was little, they would feed each other French fries, alternating one for one and dipping them sometimes in ketchup and sometimes in the Frosty.

At their last visit she let him eat the whole order, shook her head when he offered her one. She had known he'd rather have a burger. Him being a growing teenager and all that. She could tell he was eating slowly on purpose. It was a trick they both knew, stretching the visitation time, pretending there were more fries in the bag when all they were doing was eating air. She looked out the window at Corky sitting in her car. Corky smiled, held up the back of her hand and tapped her wrist as if she were wearing a watch. Times up. Missy walked with Miles to the parking lot and watched as he got into the car with Corky. Once the state-issued Prius pulled out onto Rainier Avenue and turned across the traffic into the south bound lanes, Missy slipped back into the Wendy's bathroom and shed her visiting uniform.

Missy can't stop thinking about all those years of visits at the same skanky Wendy's on Rainier as she watches Miles jog and weave his way out of the Jungle. She used to keep a notebook, write in it after every visit, sure that it would someday provide crucial evidence in her defense, and show that she was somebody's mother. She had let herself believe that people were changeable, like the weather. Such bullshit optimism. She's over it. She will not make the same mistake again, not at Miles' expense. Shit, how hadn't she seen it? There's no difference between any of them; her dad, Corky, herself, the judge, and now Miles. All the same players. All they'd done was swap out positions on the field. She knows they won't give him back, not now or ever.

Missy stops showing up at the Wendy's or at Corky's office for any sort of scheduled visit or meeting. It all goes in the file. With Missy gone, Miles is in Corky's office and Juvie more now than ever, perpetually between placements. He is *legally free*. That was what the judge's piece of paper said, his golden ticket into a real family. But he knows Missy is real. He sees her, even if no one else does. He remembers how she'd let the water run in the metal sink in the public restroom at Bradner Gardens till it was warm enough to make him hot chocolate. How she would hoist him up against the edge of the sink so he could hold his hands under the warming tap. How they would stay there all night curled together on the cement floor watching as the headlights from passing cars lit up the colorful tile walls.

He has been lying on top of the red vinyl sleeping bag in the corner of Corky's office, his feet and ankles extending way beyond the zippered bottom of the bag. He has been listening to Corky on the phone sell his assets and minimize his liabilities to group home after group home.

"He's clean, yes both, hygiene and drugs. He goes to school, most of time. Yes, grades passable. Yes, yes, he is a runner, but his UA's are clean when he comes back. Don't know where he goes; he won't say." But he knows she has her suspicions. "Yes, in care off and on since age five. Lots of placements. Mom stopped showing up for visits about six months ago, so you won't have to transport him."

"I gotta go piss."

She nods.

And off he goes down the hall and out the door. The #7 bus pulls to the curb —

perfect timing—and he's gone.

Back in the office, Corky hangs up the phone and turns to look out the window. She doesn't even register the empty bus stop. She spaces out, staring blankly, thinking first of nothing and then making a list in her head. She picks up her pen to transfer the list to a post-it: gas, bank, eggs, milk, Advil. It's forty-five minutes before she realizes Miles hasn't come back, and all she feels is relief. She will get to leave at five o'clock instead of having to stay till eight when the after-hours staff are scheduled to come in and take charge of Miles and the other three children slumped in the molded plastic chairs in the waiting room.

Miles used to be so easy to place. No trouble at all. He was small, scrawny but in a cute way. His racial make-up was ambiguous enough to put the mostly white foster parents at ease. The black foster parents recognized him as one of their own. He made a good first impression, arriving at each new place wearing his purple power ranger backpack. He was not much taller than the Hefty garbage bag sitting next to him filled with his pillow, comforter, sweatpants and t-shirts. But now he is pushing 5'9 and 150 lbs., the beginning of stubble darkening his skin. She keeps forgetting to buy him a razor.

Corky shoves Miles' file into her tote bag promising no one but herself that she will make a few more calls tonight from home, find him a place that won't be too freaked out by him. She'd like him to spend all of 8th grade at the same school. She'd like him to stop growing. She'd like him to survive long enough to make it out of her own dubious care.

Miles rides the bus all the way to the transit center, jumps off and catches the next bus south into Georgetown. He gets off and scuttles up Lucile Street, making his way into the southern outskirts of The Jungle. It's early November and almost five o'clock. It looks like night under the viaducts. The sun rides so low in the south that dusk can't find its way through the maze of concrete above his head.

Missy isn't where she was the last time he found her. The tent with the blue tarp is gone and an old Asian guy sits on a folding camp chair with his feet up on a plastic milk carton smoking. He grips an almost full pack of American Spirits in his right hand. The ground is damp. The smell of the place is everywhere. Wet and rodent.

"What are you doing here, kid? I can give you a cigarette, nothing else." Miles keeps his voice low, whispery, the voice he used to have, high and sweet,

not scary.

"You seen my mom?"

"No moms down here."

"She used to live here, tan tent, blue tarp?"

"What's she look like?"

"Small, red hair, keeps it pulled..."

"Jesus, boy, that little girl's your mom?"

"Uh, yeah, whatever. You seen her?"

"She's around here somewhere, hangs with a guy called Culhane, a real asshole. Ask around you'll find them."

Miles wanders down the embankment, his sweatpants snagging on blackberry vines. He stumbles and trips on the roots of an old vine maple stunted for lack of sun. He enters another cluster of tents and old mattresses. Grocery carts are piled high with plastic sacks filled with clothes, cans of food, shit-covered toilet paper. He finds her sitting cross-legged on her coat in front of a mound of blankets. Her head is slumped on her chest, her red ponytail looped up and over not quite dragging in the dirt. He sits across from her and crosses his legs too. Waits. His elbows are on his knees, and he rests his chin in his cupped hands, not quite mirroring her.

She must sense he is there because she comes to with a violent shrug and rears up. Her ponytail flips back into place. The freckled skin of her face is bruised yellow and purple, and her left eye is swollen shut. Her right eye is wide open, the pupil clear, alert.

"Fuck, baby boy, what are you doing here? You scared me shitless."

"Nothing Ma, I just wanted to see you. See if you're okay. You okay?"

"It's nothing." Her hand flutters around her eye and he sees it is scabbed and bloody like the side of her face.

"Shit, Ma, your hand…"

"I told you it's nothing."

She shoves the offending hand into the pocket of her thermal-lined hot-pink hoody, stretching it tight across her scrawny chest, one side covered in a big white "P I" the other "N K."

Her voice softens. "Really Miles, what are you doing here?"

He doesn't know the answer. The new gentleness in her voice makes him feel like he needs to puke, signals to him that she knows about the judge's order, and probably even agreed to it. It's like one of those tests the therapists give him year after year to determine if he still knows how to bond or if he is permanently broken. He knows the answers he should give to get a house with his own room, to get adopted. He can't bring himself to say what they want. The feel of cool leafy underbrush, his small body warm, zippered tight inside Missy's hoodie, always crowds back in. The dirt fresh smell of her skin defeats his psychological scores.

He used to be so good at it. Corky's file was filled with lots of *good little boy* statements. Here now, with Missy, he has no idea what she wants to hear.

So he mutters, "I don't know, whatever."

"Did someone hurt you, baby?

"No, Ma, I'm fine. What about your eye?" He blurts the last part out.

"I told you. It's nothing."

Missy lifts her hand to her mouth, squeezes her eyes shut. She is concentrating, trying hard not to say one more word. There is so much she wants to know. But if she asks even one question, learns even one small new thing about him, she is sure she will die, so she bites down on the edge of her hand and opens her eyes.

Miles lowers his own eyes. He is careful not to spook her again. He is okay with this. Sitting here, inches from her, not touching.

There is movement behind her, and that quick she is on high alert. He realizes the mound he thought was blankets is a person. Missy is up on her feet, yanking his arm. Miles is stiff with the damp cold and from sitting like a pretzel. He stumbles, then reaches his full height more than a head taller than her. But Missy has always been stronger than she looks. She grips him tightly by the elbow, expertly steering him through the length of the encampment. She dodges and steps lightly between tents and mattresses, doesn't slow down for more than a mile until they scramble up another embankment where the hillside gives way to the tidy manicured park that runs along I-90, grass clipped, flowering bushes, a painted pagoda, a fancy sign: *Daejeon Park Pavilion, Park Closed 11:30PM—4AM.*

"You know where you are?"

"Yeah." He's been here before.

"Good. Now go."

She doesn't say she'll see him around. She half hugs, half shoves him forward into the park and he stumbles to his knees a few feet from a couple making out. When he regains his footing and turns, she is gone.

He walks up the broad wooden steps that lead into the rounded wooden pagoda. He sits down and then lays back in the middle of the ornate floor, looking up at the painted wooden beams, the geometric designs. He sits back up. Digs around in his pack for a Moon Pie. It is dry. The cake chalky.

The stale marshmallow and chocolate all clump together at the back of his throat, and lodge in his chest. He gags and spits the shit-brown mess into his hand and flings the chunks over the railing. Slumping back down, he thinks about Missy, and all the ways they are alike, and about how people are changeable just like the weather.

He briefly considers staying in the pagoda through the night, ignoring the sign, but seconds later, he gets up and leaves the well-built shelter that no one is supposed to sleep in. The air smells clean, not like piss at all.

A month from now the city will bring in backhoes and sweep The Jungle up: tents, mattresses, shopping carts, and some old guy sound asleep in a blackberry thicket. All of it gone and crushed including the old man. They will seed the ground with truckloads of broken rock and chunks of asphalt so no one can sit down much less pitch a tent. They will erect miles of aluminum fence and roll out whorls of razor wire that look like a skin shredding version of the expandable toy tunnels Miles used to play in with Missy on rainy days at the Community Center.

He is on the verge of something. In a short time, Corky will find him a placement out in the suburbs with two nice gay men who want to be dads and practice on him. They will prove they aren't perverts and worthy of the kind of little boy Miles used to be.

He doesn't know any of this. Instead, he is thinking about the snacks he will bring Missy the next time he comes here. He is thinking about how he might scrounge together enough money to buy her a new tent. He wonders what a tent costs. He wonders what happened to the old one.

Rayme—A Memoir of the Seventies

Jayne Anne Phillips

In West Virginia in 1974 we were all in need of fortune-tellers. No one was sure what was happening in the outside world and no one thought about it much. We had no televisions and we bought few newspapers. Communal life in Morgantown seemed a continual dance in which everyone changed partners, a patient attempt at domesticity by children taking turns being parents. We were adrift but we were together. A group of us floated between several large ramshackle houses, houses arranged above and below each other on steep streets: a gritty version of terraced dwellings in some exotic Asia. The houses were old and comfortable, furnished with an accumulation of overstuffed chairs and velveteen sofas gleaned from rummage sales. There were no curtains at the large windows, whose rectangular sooty light was interrupted only by tangles of viney plants. The plants were fed haphazardly and thrived, like anything green in that town, enveloping sills and frames still fitted with the original wavy glass of seventy years before. The old glass was pocked with flaws and minute bubbles, distorting further the vision of a town already oddly displaced and dreamed in jagged pieces. Houses of the student ghetto were the landscape of the dream—a landscape often already condemned.

I lived in a house on Price Street with three male housemates: a Lebanese photographer from Rochester, New York, a Jewish instructor of transcendental meditation from Michigan, and a carpenter-musician, a West Virginian, who'd worked in the doomed McCarthy campaign and dropped out of Harvard Law to come home and learn house-building.

This story could be about any one of those people, but it is about Rayme and comes to no conclusions.

Perhaps the story is about Rayme because she lived in all the communal houses at one time or another. Intermittently, she lived with her father and stepmother and brother. Or she lived with one of her two older sisters, who had stayed in town and were part of our group of friends. Or she lived in her own small rooms, a bedroom, kitchen and bath in a house chopped into three or four such apartments. She lived alone in several of those single-person places, and in all of them she kept the provided mattress and box springs tilted upright against the wall. She slept on a small rug which she unrolled at night, or she slept on the bare floor with the rug precisely folded as a pillow. She shoved most of the other furniture into a corner or put it outside on the porch. Skirts and coats on hangers, swatches of fabric, adorned the walls. Rayme brought in large branches, a brick, a rock. Usually there were no utilities but running water; her father paid the rent and that is all that was paid. She wore sweaters and leggings and burned candles for light. She used the refrigerator as a closet for shoes and beads and seemed to eat almost nothing. She kept loose tea and seeds in jars and emptied coffee cans which she filled with nutshells and marbles.

A long time ago her mother had committed suicide in Argentina. No one ever talked about the death, but one of Rayme's sisters told me the suicide was slow rather than overtly violent. 'She stopped eating, she'd been sick, she wouldn't go to the hospital or see a doctor,' the sister said. 'It took her several months to do it.' Rayme seldom mentioned her mother and didn't seem certain of any particular chain of events concerning the past. The facts she referred to at different times seemed arbitrary, they were scrambled, they may have been false or transformed. It is true that her parents married each other twice and divorced twice; the father was a professor, the mother had musical talent and four children. Rayme told me her father wouldn't let his wife play the piano; he locked the baby grand because she became too 'detached' when she played.

The first time her parents divorced, Rayme was six years old, the only child to go with her mother. They lived alone together in Kansas. Rayme didn't remember much about it. She said sometimes she came home from school and the door was locked and she would sit outside past dark and listen to the owls in the trees. Once there was a tornado in Kansas; Rayme's mother opened all the windows 'so the wind can blow *through* the house instead of breaking it.' Then they sat on the sofa wrapped in their winter coats, rather than hiding in the basement, so they could watch the rattling funnel cloud twist and hop across the flat fields behind the town.

In Kansas, Rayme said her mother kept things, like bracelets and rings, costume jewelry, under the pillows of the bed. They used to play games with those things before they went to sleep at night and tell stories. Rayme slept by the wall because her mother sleepwalked and needed a clear path to the open.

At the time of the second divorce, Rayme was twelve. She said her father stood in the middle of the living-room and called out the names of the children. He pointed to one side of the room or the other. 'When we were lined up right, he said *those* kids would stay with him and *those* kids would go with her.' Rayme went to Argentina with her mother and oldest sister. A family friend there paid airplane fares and found housing; Rayme's father paid child support. Rayme learned some Spanish songs. Her sister went out on chaperoned dates; there was a terrace; it was sunny. Their mother died down there after a few months, and the two children came back on a boat, unchaperoned.

Rayme's sister told me Rayme didn't react when their mother died. 'Everyone else cried, but Rayme didn't. She just sat there on the bed. She was our mother's favorite.' The funeral was in Argentina, and the service was Catholic. 'I was standing by the door while the priest was in the bedroom,' Rayme's sister said.

'Rayme looked up at me wearing our mother's expression, on purpose, to say *I'd* lost my mother but *she* hadn't.'

Once Rayme sent her oldest sister a group of wallet-sized photographs in the mail. They were all pictures of Rayme taken in various years by public school photographers, and they were all dotted with tiny pinholes so that the faces were gone. Another time she came to her sister's Christmas party with one eyebrow shaved off. Her sister demanded that she shave the other one off as well so at least they'd match, and Rayme did.

Sometime late that winter, Rayme went to stay in the country at the cabin of a friend. She was living there alone with her cat; she said she could marry the snow. The cat wandered into the woods and Rayme wandered down the middle of the dirt road six miles to the highway. There was rain and a heavy frost, sleet flowers on the pavement. Rayme wore a summer shift and a kitchen knife strapped to her arm with leather thongs. She had hacked her waist-length hair to the shape of a bowl on her head and coiled her thick dark braids tightly into the pockets of her dress.

She had nothing to say to the farm couple who found her sitting on the double line of the highway in a meditative pose, but she did nod and get into the car as though expecting them. They took her to the university hospital and she committed herself for three weeks. I visited her there; she sat stiffly by a window reinforced with chicken wire between double panes, her back very straight, her hands clasped. She said it was important to practice good posture, and she moved her head, slowly, deliberately, when she looked to the right or left. Her skin was pale and clear like white porcelain. Before I left, we repeated some rituals evolved earlier in half-serious fun: children's songs with hand motions ('here is the church and here is the steeple…I'm a little teapot, short and stout…along came the rain and washed the spider out'), the Repulse Tiger movement from T'ai Chi, a series of Chinese bows in slow motion. She said the hospital was like a big clock and she was in the floor of the clock; every day she went to Group and played dominoes in the common room. She ate her lunch in a chair by the nurses' desk; she liked their white clothes and the sighing of the elevators.

By the time she was released, the TM instructor living at Price Street had moved to Cleveland. Rayme moved in with me, with the Harvard carpenter, with the Lebanese photographer. She wasn't paying rent, but we had the extra room anyway and sometimes she cooked meals.

Once she cooked soup. For an hour, she stood by the stove, stirring the soup in a large, dented kettle. I looked into the pot and saw a jagged object floating among the vegetables. I pulled it out, holding the hot thin edge: it was a large fragment of blackened linoleum from the buckling kitchen floor.

I asked Rayme how a piece of the floor got into the soup.

'I put it there,' Rayme said.

I didn't answer.

'It's clean,' Rayme said, 'I washed it first,' and then, angrily, 'If you're not going to eat my food, don't look at it.'

That was her worst summer. She told me she didn't want to take the Thorazine because it made her into someone else. Men were the sky and women were the earth; she liked books about Indians. She said cats were good and dogs were bad; she hated the lower half of her body. She didn't have lovers but quietly adored men from her past—relatives, boyfriends, men she saw in magazines or on the street. Her high-school boyfriend was Krishna, a later one Jesus, her father 'Buddha with a black heart'. She built an altar in her room out of planks and cement blocks, burned candles and incense, arranged pine needles and pebbles in patterns. She changed costumes often and moved the furniture in her room several times a day, usually shifting it just a few inches. She taped pictures on her wall: blue Krishna riding his white pony, Shiva dancing with all her gold arms adorned, Lyndon Johnson in glossy color from *Newsweek*, cutouts of kittens from a toilet-paper advertisement. Her brother, three years younger than she and just graduated from high school, came to see her several times a week. He brought her a blue bottle full of crushed mint and played his guitar. He seemed quiet, witty, focused; he looked like Rayme, the same dark hair and slender frame and chiseled bones. She said he was the angel who flew from the window with sleep-dust on his shoes; he used to tell his sisters, when they were all children, that he was the one who'd sealed their eyes shut in the night, that they would never catch him because boys could be ghosts in the dark.

On an afternoon when we'd taken mescaline, Rayme sat weeping on the couch at Price Street. The couch was brown and nubby, and people had to sit towards its edge, or the cushions fell through to the floor. The cushions had fallen through, and Rayme sat in the hole of the frame comfortably, her legs splayed up over the board front. She sat looking at the ceiling, her head thrown back like a woman trying to keep her mascara from running. She remained still, as though enthroned, waiting, her face wet, attentive. I watched her from across the room. 'Yes,' she said after a long while, as though apprehending some truth, 'tears wash the eyes and lubricate the skin of the temples.'

All of us were consulting a series of maps bearing no relation to any physical geography, and Rayme was like a telephone to another world. Her messages were syllables from an investigative dream, and her every movement was precise, like a driver unerringly steering an automobile by watching the road through the rear-view mirror.

I'd met her when we were both working at Bonanza Steak House as servers. She liked the cowboy hats and the plaid shirts with the braid trim, and she insisted on completing the outfit by wearing her brother's high-heeled boots and a string tie from Carlsbad Caverns emblazoned with a tiny six-gun. She got away with these embellishments of restaurant policy because her compulsions seemed harmless. She would stand erect behind plates of crackling steaks bound for numbered trays, looking intently into the vacuous faces of customers shuffling by in the line. She did tap-dance steps in place, wielding her spatula and tipping her hat, addressing everyone as Sir or Madam. She liked the ritual of the totally useless weekly employee meetings, in which skirt lengths and hairnets and customer quota were discussed. She admired the manager and called him Mr. Fenstermaker, when everyone else referred to him derisively as Chester, after the gimp on *Gunsmoke*. He was a fat doughy boy about thirty years old who walked around what he called 'the store' with a clipboard of names and work hours. During meetings, Rayme sat at his elbow and took down his directives in careful, cursive script, posting them later on the door to the employees' bathroom. She also posted the covers of several *True Romance* comic books. She got in trouble once for mixing the mashed potatoes with nutmeg and banana slices, and again when she arranged the plastic steak tags across the raw meat in a mandala bordered by white stones. In the centre of the mandala was the small, perfect egg of a bird. The egg was purely blue; on it Rayme had painted a Chinese word in miniature gold characters. Later she told me she'd looked the word up especially in a language textbook; the word meant *banquet*.

Rayme was protected at Price Street. She stopped losing jobs because she stopped having them; instead, she worked in the tumbledown garden, tying tomato plants to poles with strips of heavy satin and brocade—draperies she'd found in a junk pile. Meticulously, she cut the fabric into measured lengths and hemmed the pieces. She kept the house full of wild flowers and blossoming weeds, and hung herbs to dry in the hallways. The summer was easy. No one expected her to talk on days when she didn't speak. She was calm. She pretended we were mythical people and brought us presents she'd made: a doll of sticks and corn silk, with a shard of glass for a face, or the skeleton of a lizard laid out perfectly in a velvet-lined harmonica box.

In late August we were told that Price Street and the abandoned houses near it would be demolished by the city, 'to make the city hospital a more attractive property.' The rest of us complained resignedly but Rayme made no comment; quietly, she began staying awake all night in the downstairs of the house. Day after day, we awoke to find the furniture turned over and piled in a heap, the rugs rolled up, pictures turned upside-down on the walls. She took personal possessions from the bedrooms, wrapped them in her shirts and jeans, and tied the carefully-folded parcels with twine. We called a house meeting to discuss her behavior, and Rayme refused to attend. She went upstairs and began throwing plates from the windows.

We asked her brother to come to Price Street and talk to her. They sat in her room for a couple of hours, then they came downstairs. Rayme said she didn't have any money, maybe she'd live with her sister for a while. She unwrapped the stolen possessions with great ceremony and gave them back to us as gifts while her brother watched, smiling. At midnight, we made wheat pancakes and ate them with molasses, Indian-style, on the dark porch.

Several years later, when all the houses we'd lived in together had been torn down, Rayme's brother would shoot himself with a pistol. He would do it beside a lean-to he'd built as a squatter at an isolated camp site, five miles up a steep mountain trail. He would leave no notes; his body would not be discovered for some time. When they did find him (they meaning people in uniforms), they would have trouble getting a stretcher down the path and over the rocks.

But this was before that. It was September of 1974, most of us would leave town in a few weeks, and I had been recently pregnant. Some of us were going to Belize to survive an earthquake. Some of us were going to California to live on 164th Street in Oakland. A few were staying in West Virginia to continue the same story in even more fragmented fashion. My lover, the carpenter, was going to Nicaragua on a house-building deal that would never materialize. We'd had passport photos taken together; he would use his passport in the company of someone else and I would lose mine somewhere in Arizona. But on this day in September, I had never seen Arizona, and we all went to a deserted lake to swim despite the fact the weather had turned.

I remember going into the lake first, how the water was warmer than the air. On the bank the others were taking off their clothes—denim skirts and jeans, soft, worn clothes, endlessly utilitarian. Their bodies were pale and slow against the dark border of the woods. They walked into the lake separately, aimlessly, but Rayme swam straight towards me. It was almost evening and the air smelled of rain. Noise was muffled by the wind in the leaves of the trees, and when Rayme was suddenly close the splash of her movement was a shock like waking up. Her hands brushed my legs—her touch underwater as soft as the touch of a plant—and she passed me, swimming deeper, swimming farther out.

I wanted to stand on something firm and swam to the dock, a stationary thickness for mooring motorboats. It stretched out into the water a long distance. Who had built it in this deserted place? It was old, the weathered black of railroad ties. I pulled myself on to the splintery wood and began to walk along its length, touching the pylons, hearing the *swak* of stirred water as the storm blew up, hearing my own footsteps. Where were we all really going, and when would we ever arrive? Our destinations appeared to be interchangeable pauses in some long, lyric transit. This time that was nearly over, these years, seemed as close to family as most of us would ever get.

Now the rain was coming from far off, sweeping across the

water in a silver sheet. The waiting surface began to dapple, studded with slivers of rain. Rayme was a white face and shoulders, afloat two hundred yards out.

'Janet,' she called across the distance, 'when you had your abortion, did you think about killing yourself?'

'No,' I yelled back. 'Come out of the water.'

The Light of Stars, Yes

Melanie Rae Thon

1.

My brother kneels in the back of the Chrysler. Leo Derais, eleven years old: he's skipped three grades: this fall he'll start high school.

He's just made the most astonishing discovery, has seen the evidence and understands at last how time moves at different speeds in both directions. (Was that a stone? Is that a rabbit?)

Appears to move.

Quickly now, before the light goes, he wants our father to see what he sees, the earth close to the car ripping backward (skull of a desert fox, bones of a missing child), everything lost, the past shredded and gone (blink of an eye, stuttering heartbeat) while at the same time, in the same world, a ridge of distant mountains unscrolls, quietly revealing itself, advancing slowly forward.

No matter how fast our father drives, the patient line of stone proceeds, always beyond, always ahead of us. He's trembling now but can't speak. Time does not exist. Time is perception, the endless rearrangement of things in space, the infinite possibilities of their relationships to one another.

A word will shatter thought: skull, stone, star, rabbit: everything here, now, lost and still to come in this moment. There's no reason why he can't remember the future. Even now the light of stars long dead streaks toward him.

Our father, our pilot, delivers us into a night too beautiful to imagine: blue, blue sky, mountains deepening to violet.

Mother unbuttons her blouse to nurse the baby. Joelle, my sister, eleven months old, eight years younger than I am, my father's bewildered surprise, my mother's joyful mystery, Joelle Derais, so radiant strangers stop us on the street and ask to touch or try to talk to her.

If she were alive now, would she be like me, or still be tempting?

I remember her that day at the rest stop: cheeks flushed, lips rosy, the soft swirl of dark curls at the crown of her head (where I kiss, where I smell you), Joelle, my sister, heavy in my arms, heavy in my lungs, the sweet almond scent of you.

I remember the woman who gasped in the bathroom, whose fingers fluttered as she touched Joelle's warm shoulder. *My God is that child real?* She thought my sister was a doll, perfect porcelain, perfectly painted, someone else's real hair, someone else's silky lashes:

My God how porcelain shatters.

Mother wants to stop in Page, just south of the Utah border, high on this plateau of red rock where a pink neon sigh blinks *EZ REST* and a green one warns *DESPERADO'S HIDEAWAY.*

Our pilot won't rest; our desperado won't take refuge.

If time does not exist, there must be a place where I can go, where I can find us, where my sister cries and my brother trembles, where bands of rose and gold and turquoise throb at the horizon, where my father turns back, and my mother forgives him. (Somewhere in the night, while I sleep, this happens.)

Forty years. I have these words. I know these numbers. The morning paper my proof: *Oil Spilling, Bees Vanishing. Five Illegal Immigrants Found Dead, Problem Bear Relocated.*

The headline never says: *Invasive Humans Removed from Bear's Natural Habitat.*

EZ REST: I almost remember the sign flashing all night, the room that smelled of smoke and ammonia.

No. We didn't turn. The blue Chrysler sped into the blue night while the light of stars streaked toward us.

Forty years. I remember the taste of blood and bone, tongue cut deep, front teeth jagged, the smell of gasoline and smoke, something burning in the distance. My father tried to stand but couldn't stand, tried again and then a third time. He disappeared as smoke and came back as fire. His face flared in orange light.

How can both legs be broken?

Yes, everything here, now, again, always: the blue Chrysler ablaze, our bodies flung in the desert, the rearrangement of things, the infinite possibilities, the light of stars, yes, I have never seen so many stars anywhere, an ocean of sparkling light, stars alive and dead streaking toward us.

The baby was gone, the baby was missing. I remember Mother crawling in the sand, trying to find her, saying her name, *Joelle,* howling her name into the blue night all around us, leaving *jo— elle* vibrating through stone and star forever.

My brother rose up white and naked from his twisted body. He was perfect, so thin and pale I could see right through him. He stooped to scratch the sand with a stick. Later I understood the stick was a bone, one he'd pulled from his body.

So fast, my brother! He drew a lovely looping line crossing and recrossing, no beginning or end, some strange magic: flight of the hawk or snake coiling, a wave of sound inside a stone, breath moving between bodies.

I don't remember the days in the hospital, the nights and days I slept, brain swollen. I remember waking in my bed at home, a deer under the mesquite tree by my window, the shadows of leaves fluttering across her body: a deer in disguise: I heard her breath in my breath, felt warm blood surge through me.

Alive, I was. Even now I believe the deer's blood healed me. Mother played "Clair de Lune" on the piano with her left hand, half a song; the deer breathed in fluttery time, and I breathed with her. Doves sang missing notes, but not the right ones, not Debussy's, some startling rearrangement of sound, every song endlessly new, no matter how many times Mother played them.

Alive, yes, my mother's one, my father's only.

Blood surges from the heart and soon returns or doesn't. Forty years. At the Mission one day I watched a man restore the wounds of Jesus, scraping away oil and dirt to paint the openings again, red so red it glowed, wounds so deep blood bloomed violet.

Such love! The painter looked thin as Jesus, scarred too, hurt and hungry. Yes, here, God alive, breath inside a starved brown body. He'd repaired broken thorns and broken fingers; now, as he touched the wounds with his brush, tendons beneath flesh flickered. In a looping line of blue vein, I felt the painter's blood in me pulsing.

So easily the body opens.

The shadows of leaves become the shadows of hands, doctors' hands inside my brother's body, stitching artery and bowel, touching the soft secret skin inside the belly, hoping to stop the blood, to bring him back, to reassemble a puzzle of bone, pelvis and rib from shattered fragments.

Mother played with one hand because the right hand was crushed, the right arm splintered: *Mother*: because she held Joelle tight in her left arm, and used her right arm to brace them.

Skull of a desert fox, bones of a missing child:

There is a place I can go on that road, a line I can draw on a map: a frontier, a border: my country before, my country after: *Joelle*:

Forty years, and just today, just this morning, the song of you, a wave of sound, a coyote across the arroyo howling: Joelle:

Tonight, in the light of stars, in the light of fire, our brother kneeling in the sand, drawing a lovely looping line, no beginning or end, crossing and recrossing, to catch the breath between, to hold, to save, to lift us

Small Signals

Stephanie Dupal

At your signal, I cut the engine. I hear our truck puffing a long final scrawl of exhaust. It's the dying breath of an old friend, banged on the passenger side, its hood soldered in three distinct patches where a leak iced through rust two winters ago. In the cab, the smell of Tangerine Arbre Magique wafts when the little cardboard air freshener sways from the rearview mirror like a forlorn Christmas tree. I lean as far as I can and roll down your window. We're somewhere in the Utah desert, on our way to Lunar Crater in Nevada's Pancake Mountain range, to celebrate the start of my senior year in high school.

"Class of '87, can you believe it, Liz? It all went by so fast," you said just before the truck's engine started to sputter, and you had to pull over. Now I can hear you, Dad, cussing outside, in the September morning heat, as you bend over the intricate mess of wires, pipes, and parts, though all I see is smoke and the propped hood's rust flaking in interesting patterns on what was once a hearty tomato red. The sun's burnt the glaze off—the varnish, the veneer—whatever it's called, and in the center the metal has turned a dark orange, like autumn leaves.

I'd like to turn the keys a notch to hear if frequency can be picked up in the desert, but I'm afraid that you're tinkering with the battery, and I don't know if it's possible to get shocked from a battery. What would people listen to out here on Labor Day weekend? A local station probably plays nonstop country honky-tonk. There's always better entertainment on our Citizens Band Radio.

You taught me the CB codes and regulations, the ethics, as you say, of keeping company with strangers, on the New Year's

Eve to New Year's Day drive we did from Denver to Green River on I-70. Buddha Boy was telling us about his wife's custard cream pie waiting for him at home, asked if we'd tasted custard cream pie, and, after you replied, "Negatory, Buddha Boy," you handed me the device and said, "How about you, Hot Wheels? You ever tasted custard cream pie?" That's my handle: Hot Wheels. We don't see the people we're talking to. They don't see me in my wheelchair. They don't get the joke.

Now I take the CB receiver in my hand and outline the toy car you glued on top of it. It's a black muscle car with shooting flames on the sides. You lower the hood, pop it down twice with your hip. I sway back with the motion, holding on to the window frame. You look worn out, yet you smile.

"Hey, I think we're going to see some desert up close," you say. You come around to the driver's side wiping your hands on your thighs. "Remember last time we came through here, you said you wanted to poke around and find new ant specimens. Well, looks like we're going to do just that. You up to it?"

"Might as well. Before or after we get this thing fixed?"

"After. If it weren't for the damn truck, I tell you." You always do that, say 'I tell you,' when you just don't know how to explain what's going on. And if you take the palm of your hand to wipe across your forehead when you say it, which you do just now, then I know you're worried.

"It's not like it hasn't happened before," I say. I don't want to emphasize the fact that we're gas station latchkeys, that this time it will be harder, considering we're in the middle of nowhere and the temperature is rising. There's a good breeze, though. In an hour or two, the road will shimmer with long mirages.

"First, we need to find the You-Are-Here spot." You wink at me, placing your hand on your chin and rubbing a little with your fingertips. "We need to go in the direction of the nearest town."

I open the glove compartment, hand you our tattered *Utah, the Beehive State* map, and you unfold it on the seat. I scoot, so

I'm not sitting on Southeastern Idaho. Your finger traces the line of Highway 6, tapping along the places we've already passed.

"Jericho. About two or three miles down. We're right outside Little Sahara."

"I'm taking my notebook." I pull it out from under my seat, pressing down the curled paper edge of eleven years of ant observation. It's as thick as a ream of paper and heavy as a small puppy.

You walk to the back of the truck and open the tailgate. I can hear you slide my wheelchair on the flatbed. I pat the cover of my notebook before opening the passenger door. You unfold the chair and I drop my hands on the armrests, with my back facing the seat. It's a smooth motion until my feet hit the ground with that awkward thump. I reach up and grab my notebook from the seat. You push me around to the front of the pickup, and my wheels hit the asphalt of the road. I open my notebook to the first page, written in blue ballpoint ink. You tried to make perfect block letters so I could read the entries on my own. I had just turned six. You never corrected my sentences.

> The ants walk crazy. One ant walks around in a big circle one way and then the other way. Ants carry things bigger than their bodies. I haven't seen an ant eat. All they do is walk in circles and carry things. If you kill an ant, if an ant gets killed by accident, another ant will get another ant, and they carry the body down to the place where they have the funerals. Their antennas move around their head a lot. I think that's how they talk to each other. They send signals. We can't hear them. They're very small signals.

You look over my shoulder. "Never knew a kid who wanted to know so much." You wipe your brow with your sleeve and take off your yellow Mack cap. You graze the stubble on your chin with its plastic snap-on straps and it sounds like a cat's tongue on skin. It must be 85 degrees already. You rest your left arm on the rubber window seals of the opened driver-side door. "I'd find you poking through the grass with the telescope's magnifier.

I think you even unscrewed the bottom plate to make it easier." You lean against the door and cross your arms in front of your chest. "Look at that sky. You need to make me a description like that McCarthy fellow you were reading. What would he say about this lonely road and these here mountains of the desert?"

"You didn't even like Blood Meridian," I say. "I'm going to read you some Willa Cather when we get home. I think you'll like her better and the way she saw the West, only not the Archbishop book. I still can't finish that one. It makes me fall asleep."

"You'll have to get our trucking crew in on it, but not when they're driving." You look worried, watching the horizon in the distance. "That's all we need is to kill them with boring books about Catholics."

I shift my wheels to the left to follow grooves in the road and the herringbone of old tire marks.

When you and I travel together, like this, I read out loud and over the CB. I have six regular listeners from base unit, plus whoever tunes in to our channel. As Foxy Lady says, it's better than a book on tape, you can ask questions and you don't have to fool around with the tape deck if you've missed something. Her husband, Haywire, always agrees. "That's right, Foxy Lady, that's right." He doesn't say Big Ten-four because she's sitting next to him. Big Ten-four is code. Although its meaning will change according to the situation, it means, I hear you—I know what you're saying—I agree.

Foxy Lady made Haywire drive two straight shifts when I read Pale Horse, Pale Rider on our way to Reno in June. We kept up with their rig as best we could. When I read the part about Miranda getting the letter that said that Adam was dead, Foxy Lady cried. "Hot Wheels," Haywire said, "no more of them crazy romantic stories. Next time, we're reading some Louis L'Amour. He'd do justice to a title like Pale Horse, Pale Rider."

Haywire doesn't like it when Foxy Lady has her bleeding-heart moments, as he calls them. More than eighteen months after the Challenger burst in the air like a firecracker gone wrong, she still talks of the schoolteacher who died with the crew. For some reason, that woman pulls at her. She never speaks to us of the long lines of pinkish smoke, the contrails of cotton candy that we saw night after night on television, but she talks about that schoolteacher, and Haywire just says, "Hush now, darling, hush. She's teaching all the baby angels in heaven now. Believe you me, lady." When he calms her down like that, I imagine her leaning on his shoulder while he drives.

"Let's get this show rolling," you say.

In the distance, a buzzard perches on a tree. He is a silhouette against the dust and the sky's dry white. On the other side of the road, the Rockies block the horizon far off to the east. What I like about being here is the long quiet. The long quiet is a different kind of silence than not hearing anything, because it's the sound of things you can't see. Everywhere has its own long quiet.

The buzzard sits still. I need a wingspan. I've always wanted to start ornithology, however difficult that research would be for me. The shots from Mutual of Omaha's Wild Kingdom are always the same: scruffy-looking bird lovers wearing thigh-high rubber boots wade deep in marshlands, with various sets of binoculars hanging round their necks. Look at that Great Heron, the man with the beard whispers to the camera. It's a beauty.

I open my notebook to a blank page and write:

Saturday, September 5, 1986. Highway 6. Three miles north of Jericho. (Find nomenclature.) Buzzard: most likely male, rich brown plumage. Could be mottled, not able to tell from the distance, about 250 ft. Light underside. Perched at top of bush. Does not move. Watches. Calculates.

I can hear you behind me fussing with the keys and the ignition, trying to get the CB to work. I flip through pages of my notebook, looking up at intervals to see the buzzard. In my handwriting, I read an entry for my first ant farm.

Carpenter Ant Farm of Elizabeth Fraser

Day One

The ants are beginning to branch out west. They are slightly larger than the backyard ants. Six years of backyard research isn't like this slice of glass. I need a cross-section of the backyard.

I'm tempted to cross out some minor mistakes in many of these pages, but that would be misleading foundation work. It took me a few years to get their rituals down. During the third year of the carpenter colony, the queen died. This is, by far, the most critical moment for any colony. Authoritative transference.

Year 3, Month 10, Day 5

The queen has died. The workers came within minutes and they held a council. The worker I marked with a yellow paint dot is taking the lead. She's tapped the others with her antennae and she even redirected one with her mandible. I observed them for four consecutive hours. The yellow dot ant pressed the others to move the queen to the refuse chamber. The dead queen lay among the tiny droppings of her people. Three princesses are waiting to shed their wings, to see who will be next, who will be queen.

Year 3, Month 10, Day 6

The queen's body has disappeared. I can't see the yellow dot ant. One of the princesses removed her wings. She must have been fertilized. I missed the mating, probably happened last night while I was sleeping. Just like that: new monarchy. It's 11:35 p.m. and I can't stay up any longer. I've just come back from the fair and I missed the queen's burial.

Year 3, Month 10, Day 7

The yellow dot ant resurfaced. A few soldiers are circling the colony's entry. By order of the yellow dot ant? The new queen selected her quarters. I can't see her. She's covered the glass with dust while nesting. It's only a matter of time before one of her workers cleans her quarters. It's only a matter of time before the yellow dot ant takes over the colony.

"Breaker One-nine, does anyone have a copy for this here Sandman?"

"Ten-four, Sandman. This is Card Dealer, good buddy." His voice crackles with static.

"What's your Ten-twenty, Car Dealer?"

"Northbound on 6, about to pass Jericho Junction."

You turn up the squelch and you can still hear Card Dealer, without the static. "Car Dealer, my girl and I are stuck southbound with a pickup that quit on us. Can you mark time from Jericho to where we're at?"

"I think he's saying Card Dealer, Dad."

"Ten-four, good buddy. You want me to send a Ten-two-hundred, Sandman?"

"Negatory. My girl and I are going back to Jericho and getting some lunch. You know if there's a mechanic down there?"

"Passing Jericho, Sandman, starting the count. Don't know about a mechanic. Big Texaco and diner though."

I look up to see my buzzard, and he takes flight.

Flight: swoops down, four measured beats of wings and picks up speed, height. Slows down flapping. A nice span, even breadth, nice regular rhythm.

I sketch his outline. I have to be fast. With my left hand on the rubber, I turn as best I can to follow him, and with my right, I fill out his silhouette. On the horizon, I see the metal of an 18-wheeler coming toward us. The sun flicks on the wheeler until it's about three hundred feet away, and then it starts to slow down. The steamy hoot of brakes simmers down, stops.

Card Dealer's wheeler has custom airbrushing on the cab, a painting of a straight flush. Card Dealer opens the door and drops his legs and the rest of his body from his seat. He has to use the footrest. He's a fifty-something trucker with a belt buckle the size of my fist. There's an eagle head on his buckle, a full-bodied eagle tattooed on his left arm, and an ace of spades on his right forearm. The ink's old and blue.

"Sandman," Card Dealer says, looking back and forth between the two of us. "Let me turn my baby around and get you folks back to the Texaco." He pulls on his right earlobe, no longer looking at me. "It'd be my pleasure."

"Thanks, buddy, but my girl and I are going to make it on our own." You nod to me and raise your left eyebrow twice, which I understand as a sign not to argue with you. "What's the count?"

"About 2.8 miles from here. You know, it'd be my pleasure to take you there."

"That's all right. It'll take us fifty minutes to an hour." You pat Card Dealer on the shoulder and he does the same, like two chiefs leaving for war.

Card Dealer gets back in his rig. He pokes his head out the window and tells us to take care. You thank him. I wave. When he starts up the road, he honks three times.

"Why'd you say no to him?"

"You're a pretty girl, just like your mother."

I sigh. The ghost of the great Cynthia makes her appearance. "What's that supposed to mean?"

"He offered help a little too quickly. You can't trust anyone, even if you think they're good people. Nothing's what it seems sometimes."

I trace the stitching on my armrest. "He saw a poor girl in a wheelchair. He felt sorry for us."

"Well, we aren't taking a chance on sorry."

We don't say anything else for a while. The small of my back is damp, and my shirt sticks to my skin. I can feel sweat pearl on my forehead. The temperature keeps rising. The buzzard reappears. He's circling overhead. "Push me, will you?"

I start tracing circles. How does the circle work? Does it move along, forming an invisible spiral? I scribble a few notes here and there on the flight diagram.

"What's that you're doing there?"

"Buzzard." I point.

"Did you know I had a hawk like that when I was a kid?"

"You said your mom kept finches in a white cage, but nothing about hawks."

"Little buzzard, kind of looked like that one, smaller though. Wasn't really mine, you know. I just picked him up on a deer hunt. He had a broken wing. I got a book from the library, and I started to feed him."

"Good for you." There's no cheer or encouragement in my voice. You don't notice, pushing me along this long road to nowhere.

"Kept him in a big moving box with a blanket inside. In the garage. You know grandma." You sigh.

"And you killed it."

You stop pushing. "Why do you think that? It didn't die. I took him to wildlife rescue. Somebody had to fix his wing. What'd you think, I'd be able to keep it? He only stayed with us for a week."

I want to say that the course of nature isn't always so kind, but I don't, so you don't return to the subject of my mother and her accidental death. I turn the pages of the notebook. How many times have I seen the cruelty of nature in my own life and in the lives of my ants?

Year 3, Month 12, Day 20

I introduced the larvae of the same species into the colony. Within an hour, they have been transported down. I can't see anything.

Year 3, Month 12, Day 21

Soldier ants are making reconnaissance. They divide into files and explore the top of a container they should know by heart. The workers are busy readjusting a tunnel. They clear up an area of glass. Yesterday's larvae are dead. I will not introduce new ants to the colony. Their chemical composition must be different. The larvae were of the same species but of a different colony.

Each colony has its own smells, its own signals, its own ways of protecting its interests. Some of the soldiers file back down. What were they looking for? More queer-smelling larvae?

"You know, there's a place around here near Delta that has trilobites hidden all over," you say. "It's called Trilobite Mountain. I hear Topaz Mountain is nearby and you can pick topaz bits on the trail."

Here, cruelty: minute, quick. Places I can't go.

"We'll go there sometime. We'll get ourselves some trilobites and some topaz. I've been there a while back. I must have been your age. We hiked Notch Peak. You walk up a trail for about three fourths of the way, and then you hit rock formation and you climb. At the top, it's a sheer drop on one side. You can see the Sevier for miles and salt deposits shine like crazy. It's real pretty. You'd like it good."

"Notch Peak. Never heard of it." I'll never go there. Sometimes I think you forget, though I know it's probably always on your mind: the things we can't do. And just when I think that I'm about to start crying over a dumb mountain I can't climb, you make the ghost of my mother appear again.

"You know what your mother did at the wedding?"

I don't know why you think that her memory soothes me when, in fact, it soothes only you. "You told me already."

"If you don't want to hear it."

Now you're hurt. You'll go quiet on me for hours. You know I can't stand that, so I'll humor you. It's the only thing I can do when you and I are like this, when everything we've built over the years is being pulled from us because she's still on the tip of your tongue. "Go ahead."

"Your mother looks mighty fine and I'm nervous as hell. I've got a crazy shirt on with frilly ruffles and sideburns that are groomed and sharp as the devil. I think I cleaned up good."

"You looked like Robert Redford in Butch Cassidy and the Sundance Kid."

"That's what everybody said."

"I know." How many times have you asked, 'Don't you think I kind of look like good old Bob Redford in Butch Cassidy and the Sundance Kid?'" Can't you hear in my voice that I don't want to hear this? You have the look of someone walking through a fog. You're the ornithologist on Wildlife Kingdom and my mother is the rarest of birds. You advance slowly through the cadence of the story, afraid she might take flight.

"I can't remember what the minister says, but he says it. I've said my I do part and it's your mother's turn. From the second row behind us, Uncle Gerald gets up and slides to center aisle looking like he's about to croak. He's choking. He scrambles up the aisle and he keels over."

"Oh, he keels over."

"Don't poke fun. Uncle Gerald is heaving with his mouth open and awry like it's been taken off its hinge. He's not doing anything except trying to put all his fingers down his own throat. Somebody yelled 'Heimlich!' but your mother just went over to him, kneeled down, put her left hand on his forehead, and reached in and tugged out his lower bridge. Uncle Gerald had swallowed part of his bridge. That's the thing that replaces a couple of teeth, not the whole mouthful."

"Disgusting." I don't want to hear this story anymore. I'll have to think about how much you miss her. I'll have to think about how little I remember from back when there were three of us. You can't expect me to miss the woman who got herself killed and put me in this chair. All the trouble we've had because she fell asleep and drove off the road.

"Your mother, she just stands up, and she waves the bridge in front of the crowd, as if to say, Ah ha, dentures! And everybody starts clapping. We're not married yet and the guests are cheering. Uncle Gerald gives everybody a gummy smile and takes the bridge from her hand and slides it in his mouth. Cynthia and Uncle Gerald are taking a bow at our wedding. I tell you, your mother was a funny woman."

On the breeze, there's a weird, campy smell of wet earth and gasoline though there's nothing but a shack further down the road. From here, it appears like a shanty made of slats and metal. You stop walking.

"Stay here." You start running. Your boots clop like hooves, from a steady trot to a soft canter. I start pushing, trying to keep pace with the diminishing outline of your body.

"Dad!" I yell. My breath is cut short from pushing. I see you open a small door on what looks like a roof. You help a man out, pulling him out by his arms, then holding him up by his waist. The shack turns out to be an overturned trailer with a makeshift hatch made of wooden slats, like a human-sized crate of fruit. I am thirty feet away, and I hear pigs, squealing high somewhere in there. You both jump off and you sit the man down against the back of the hatch. He's only a kid my age, maybe a few years older, wearing a gray Alice Cooper t-shirt and ripped jeans, speckled in blood. He looks up at the sky and says something I can't hear. Then he folds his legs close to his body, putting his forehead on his knees.

"You okay?" I ask him.

He stares at my legs before saying no. "My old man's gonna kill me when he finds out." With both his hands, he rubs the back of his head.

I roll to the side of the trailer, putting my fingers between the horizontal slats. I feel the short, humid breath of a piglet on my left hand. He can barely wedge part of his snout in the opening. It quivers in and out with each breath.

"My dad will get you out. Don't worry, you'll be all right," I tell the pig.

"I tried to get some of them out, honest to God I did, but they got all frenzied and started trampling me down." The kid is talking more to himself than to me.

"Dad, what the hell are you doing?" I watch you pull a rifle from the cab of this kid's truck.

"You should've stayed back," you say, dangling the rifle with a steady hand. "Now go, you can't watch." You climb to the top of the hatch and open the door. "Go, I'll catch up with you." You are a different man, one capable of violence. "Wave in distress if you see a car coming." Your tone hardens. "Don't waste time."

The kid stands next to me. He puts his hand on the right handle of my chair. "I was supposed to make two trips. Take them twenty at a time for a delivery to Santaquin. Didn't want to take the whole day. I packed them all in there. All of them."

"How many?" you ask the kid.

The pigs' squealing is sickening. They shriek, some of them like newborn babies.

"Thirty-eight. I was making the bend. Next thing I know the trailer's pulling the truck off the road. I couldn't do nothing once the trailer kicked off." He makes a snaking motion with his hand, his palm flat and ready for an invisible handshake. His skin looks yellow and thick and dirty.

"Boy you're a dumb shit." You place the butt of the rifle against the hollow of your shoulder. I look between the slats. The piglet is gone.

"Dad, there was a little one on top. Get him out." I see the mass of their bodies, wriggling.

"They're all little. They're pushing each other on the broken planks. They're suffering." I hear you cock the rifle. "They'll bleed themselves to death one nick at a time."

From behind, I grab the kid's shirt. "Get on top and pull them out."

He looks at me in panic. "It's a mess. I can't do it. He's got to."

The squealing dies down. As if they know what kind of man you are, there above them, holding the gun. "Dad," I plead, "wait. There's got to be something we can do."

You ignore me and ask the kid if he has more cartridges. He rummages through the cab and brings you a brown cardboard box. The kid doesn't look at me. He hands you the box.

You take off your Mack cap and watch me with that cold

stare. Your mind is made up. The wind lifts a few strands of your hair, ringed by the band of your cap, a halo around your head. I turn to face the road and I start to cry. I feel like I'm four again, unable to do anything on my own, with the heft of dead legs weighing me down.

I turn to see you on top of the hatch and the sun blazes. You are radiant. My body shivers from fear or sadness or the tremor of my weeping. The kid puts a hand on my shoulder, but I hardly feel it.

You yell, "They're killing themselves. You can't see the blood. You can't see anything from down there."

"We can thank Mom for that!" I yell back. "You think I give a shit about your wedding?"

"Now's not the time."

"I remember her saying she wanted to drive. And you let her because she had to get her way."

"Shut your mouth, Liz."

"She screwed up our lives."

"Shut up now." You're full of anger. "I'm not going to tell you again."

"Are you going to point that thing at me like I'm a little pig?"

In answer, you aim the rifle at the squealing darkness and shoot. There's an ugliness to your face, an unnamed horror turning down the corners of your mouth. I put my hands on my ears. They ring with each shot. The air fills with the tang of gunpowder and new blood. You pause to wipe your brow.

"Fuck that bitch," I holler as loud as I can. "I'm glad she's dead!"

"I was driving!" you scream. "You don't remember any of it! We switched midway. I killed her and put you in a goddamn wheelchair because I fell asleep driving." Your shoulders fall and you whimper an incantation: "All that love, all that love." Your face is a shadow.

Nothing is as it seems, you said hours ago. Your expression

softens, and I don't want to witness the tumbling of your grief. I'd like to think that you're about to jump down to reach for me, yet I doubt that you will, so I push away and leave the scene as you wanted me to do.

The wheels turn for what feels like the longest time, until my arms ache and my muscles spasm. You, with your Custer-like knowhow of life and death, you wait until you can no longer see me before you pull the trigger again.

In the distance, I see the tall pole of the Texaco sign. The buzzard never followed. He'll watch you walk to Jericho, your hands buried deep in your pockets, while words you thought would never leave your mouth ring in your ears.

I've hated my mother all these years. It's as if my vision is now blurred, and I can't see all the ways you and I existed in this family of two. Yet the more I think of it, the more I know you are lying. Even now, you want to protect her memory, so you take the blame. I can clear the dust of our memories and know I won't find your version of our story refracted in the mirages of this burning road.

I try not to think of the pigs. I open my notebook to the progress of the yellow dot ant, before I started the harvester ant colony, before we caught three queens during their nuptial flight in the mating season. It happens every year around Labor Day with the harvester ants. We watched them fly, a cloud of insects, their little winged bodies pullulating the sky. Pullulating. That's what they did.

I wanted the yellow dot ant to succeed. I wanted it so badly that I moved some of the soldiers around, to give her space. I tampered the project.

Year 4, Month 1, Day 2

The yellow dot ant has taken over the northwest tunnels. She's been tapping and signaling for the past two days. She's rallied two workers and they've displaced the queen to a new chamber. Dragging the queen was a difficult process. Her abdomen didn't pass through her chamber door. Perhaps the message of relocation wasn't relayed properly. Bees send out scouts to map the territory around their hives. The scouts return and perform a pattern dance that tells the workers exactly where to find food, down to the nearest inch. A scientist once sent out scouts whose wings he had pulled out. They actually walked. They walked all the way to the food and in their pattern dance they expressed the time it had taken them to walk in flight time. It took hours and hours before the workers returned. They had passed the food source, unable to interpret even the slightest of signals.

It must be noon. The sun is directly overhead. The pigs could be dead by now. I'm like you with your awful lies and I'm like that kid who had somebody else put those pigs out of their misery.

The yellow dot ant died. She never took over the colony. And maybe she would have if I hadn't touched her and fooled around with the soldiers. She wouldn't have moved the queen to another chamber and I wouldn't have witnessed her demise.

My notebook, worn and sick-looking in its uneven green, sits on my lap, evidence of a cold case, of an unresolved crime. It's not just me, this notebook is tired, too, injured all these years by the way I've scribbled stupid notes. We are part of an insignificant world that refuses to change. I hold the notebook against my chest where it hurts most, and I toss it like a Frisbee. Its pages flap open with the soft whoosh of waltzing paper, as if it has wings and the sudden gift of flight. It hits the crackled dirt with a dull thud that sounds hollow. Then there's nothing left but the long quiet. Far in the distance, haze rises out the desert and dances ghostly against the sun. Even when things are hazy and out of reach, we find comfort in the stories we tell one another to keep our hearts beating. There is beauty in that, at least.

I'll get to the Texaco, tap on the glass door of the diner, look in until someone offers to help me. I'll tell the waitress behind the counter about our pickup, about Card Dealer, about a dumb teenage kid on his way to Santaquin. I'll start with the pigs. She'll make a phone call. A few truckers will listen and they'll tell stories about the time they saw turkeys running around a highway after an accident. One will say their feathers flew up over his windshield like snow. The waitress will get off the phone, hand me something to drink, for free. I will wait for you.

The Santaquin kid will offer you a ride, but you'll refuse.

I'll order a custard cream pie if they have it. While I eat the pie, you'll walk in the diner. You'll come over to my table and reveal my notebook behind your back. You'll put it in front of me, keeping your hand on the cover. You'll say, "Don't ever pull a goddamn stunt like that, Liz." There will be sadness and fear in your eyes. We won't speak of my mother again, at least for a good long while. And we'll forget the ways this story could have played out if I believed what you said.

As we sit there, you'll tell me that you felt foolish for not shooting apart the trailer earlier to let the piglets spill out on the ground, their pink bodies rolling in the dust. You'll say less than half of them died. And I'll tell you, finally, about the yellow dot ant. You'll say that everything else in the project is real. You'll say sometimes I'm just off my rocker. And we'll both laugh, yet not in the same way we used to.

After we've eaten, you and I are going to observe the diner patrons with slow and deliberate attention. You'll invite two or three of the friendly ones to join in on our next book reading, but since they work a different trucking route, they'll have to turn down your offer. We will give the rest of them names— Turkey Feathers, John Wayne, Old Yeller—western names as hardy as desert bones, blanched crisp as the napkins and paper placemats on which I'll take notes. You'll tug on your ear or scratch your nose, which we understand as signals. The diner patrons won't notice. They never do. So we'll go on speaking to each other in code.

Why Are You Here?

Mark Lammers

"If you happen to be gay," the Peace Corps trainer said during stateside orientation days before we would leave for our two-year assignments in Niger, "don't act on it or you could be jailed, even deported." I scanned the faces in the room, searching for any of the thirty-odd, soon-to-be-volunteers for someone like me. There was one, maybe two guys whom I suspected might be gay. But everyone looked straight ahead. There wasn't room for solidarity in this *Don't Ask, Don't Tell* culture that had just been described to us.

I was a 22-year-old fledgling gay man with insatiable wanderlust, a newly minted anthropology degree and one foot out of the closet. It was the end of the 80s; the Reagan-Bush era of the Moral Majority and the AIDS epidemic were all in full swing, and the idea of coming out to my parents stopped me dead in my tracks. I was ten when they separated. I had isolated myself without friends my own age. We were Midwestern, Swedish-American and didn't flaunt love, the word or the emotion. Love was assumed but never spoken. But could I assume they would love me if they knew how I felt about other men?

In my mind, Africa was idyllic. I had spent a semester in the big-sky, red-earth country of Kenya two years earlier and now wanted to return for a more authentic experience that wasn't printed on the pages of a tourist brochure. I wanted time for soul-searching, like Peter Matthiessen in *The Snow Leopard*, trekking western Nepal looking for a wild cat and grieving the loss of his wife to cancer. I also wanted to disappear, to hide from the job of living the truth. Secluding myself in the wilderness of the Sahel, the broad arid swatch of land south of the

Sahara Desert, from the Atlantic to the Red Sea, seemed like a good way to do that. I had no delusions about Third World Development. I knew I wasn't going to save the world, but still I did expect to go to Niger, lead a simple life in a Niger village, make a small impact, and figure own my own shit out along the way. Only nothing turned out the way I expected it to.

David, the Peace Corps country director, drove a white Toyota Landcruiser along a mule track through the Acacia thorn scrub. The Harmattan wind that spewed dust across the Sahara and far into the Atlantic, had blotted out the sun and turned everything a sepia tone. In the back of the truck were my only possessions—a red Honda dirt bike, my *moto*, two duffel bags, one filled with books (*One Hundred Years of Solitude*, *The Pedagogy of the Oppressed*, *The Homosexual Matri*) and another with clothes. On my lap I held a small box with a white kitten in it named Sam. I had just completed three months of in-country language and technical training and was being delivered to post, my home for the next two years.

We pulled into the village of Gabi, a collection of mud brown adobe compounds and wide sandy streets flanked by towering Baobab trees that looked as if someone had pulled them out of the ground and stuck them back in upside down. David stopped the truck in front of one of the compounds. Stepping out of the truck, I smelled woodsmoke and heard the gentle thuds of women pounding millet in wooden mortars.

Three men gathered in front of us—the *Chef du Village*, an older man dressed in flowing robes; Ibrahim, the village school teacher with bald head and three horizontal scars on each cheek; and Amadou, the owner of the house and my new housemate. *Sanu da zuwa*, they said—*welcome!* We unloaded my duffels and the *moto* and stepped into the compound. To the left two doors lead to windowless, sand-floored rooms. One would be my bedroom, the other the kitchen. Beyond the latrine—a square hole in the ground—was a bathing area for bucket showers. No running water and no electricity.

"I have to get going," David said.

I turned to look at him and swallowed hard. My safety net was leaving. The camaraderie and support of being around other English speakers in a foreign place was walking out the front door. I tried not to look as terrified as I felt. I watched as the truck pulled away. The thought of two years here stretched out before me as vast as the Sahel itself.

Ibrahim was the village school teacher, one of two people in the village who spoke French. My Hausa was basic but hardly fluent. That afternoon he helped me to set up the kitchen and bedroom. I began to unpack and bring order to my new world. I asked him about the chickens that had been gifted to me weeks earlier on my first on-site visit. I didn't know if anyone would bring me dinner and wanted to be self-sufficient on that first night.

"*Je ne sais pas,*" he said, "They could be anywhere."

I asked if he could find one for me. He sighed, turned and left the compound, returning an hour later holding an upside-down bird by the feet, wings flapping.

"I don't know how to kill a chicken," I told him. Peace Corps had given me language and technical training, taught me how to ride a *moto* through deep sand. But they hadn't taught me how to kill my own food.

"*Wallahi,*" he said, "*for God's sake,*" and left the compound again.

He returned with the dead bird, feathers scorched off. "Where is your knife," he asked poking around in a box of kitchen utensils.

"I can do it myself," I said, "I know how to cook a chicken." I wanted to tell him that at home, chicken came on Styrofoam and wrapped in plastic.

"No, I will do it," he said, grabbing a knife from a drawer to cut up the chicken. He lit the propane burner.

"You must cook it well," he told me, as the grease began to splatter from the frying pan.

I felt like I was a child watching him, my blood pressure surging. *I can do this myself,* I told myself. I didn't need his help.

When it was cooked, he flipped the chicken pieces onto a plate and handed it to me. I asked if he would join me for dinner, but he declined and walked out of the compound.

I sat down at my chair in the courtyard. It was already getting dark. I picked at the tough chicken. Who was I trying to fool? I was angry with myself for being so helpless, so dependent on others. I pushed the plate away and pulled out a pack of Rothmans cigarettes.

This self-imposed exile was what I wanted, I reminded myself—to be isolated in the wilderness of the Sahel. But the insecurity of not being in control of anything, the inability to do basic things and the uncertainty of my future burst like a wildfire in my chest. I had wanted this, I had planned for this, and I would make this happen no matter how hard it was right now.

The first few weeks in Gabi were rough. My *moto* wouldn't start half the time, and I'd get lost easily when I left the village. It also quickly became clear that I had no work to do. I had been sent to Niger as an Agro-Forestry volunteer to do three things—teach villagers how to plant trees in crop fields, introduce off-season gardening and run the village tree nursery. My housemate, Amadou, was already doing a fine job of running the tree nursery, the villagers were already practicing off-season gardening, and they refused to plant thorn trees in fields because the thorns injured their bare feet.

I started a garden of my own for something to do. In the cool of each morning, I walked to water it, passing cuvettes—basins that filled with water in the rainy season and formed small ponds. I would stop every day at one pond and sit on a fallen tree overlooking it. It was here where I centered myself, the presence of standing water was a rarity and reminded me of home. My compound was a busy place during the day with people coming and going to visit Amadou. It was there at the pond where I had privacy and could think.

One morning as I passed by the village well, a middle-aged woman with a wrinkled brow, red scarf and a smile shouted at me, "Give me those glasses."

All villagers were conservative Muslims so conversations between men and women who were not married or related weren't normal. But perhaps because she was past child-bearing years, and because I was a foreigner, she could joke with me.

"I can't see without my sunglasses," I'd said.

"*Haba*," she replied, *bullshit*.

"Why are you here?" she asked.

It wasn't like I'd never asked myself the same question every time my *moto* failed to start, every time a thorn punctured my tire, every time the chronic Giardia kicked me in the stomach, every time panic attacks sent me to my pack of Rothmans.

"Are you here to give us money?" she howled. "Give me some money!"

I was the first Peace Corps volunteer in Gabi, probably the only American she'd ever met. To her, I was a rich white guy who had come to live in this isolated and poor village for some reason incomprehensible to her. I felt like I was holding on to the edge of a cliff and she had just walked to the edge and kicked a little dirt in my face.

One Saturday a few weeks after arriving in Gabi, I returned from the post office in Magaria with a mother lode of mail. The hot season had begun, and the midday heat was suffocating. I felt as if I were standing in front of an open oven door. I pulled off my helmet, head damp from sweat, and walked into the cool darkness of my bedroom. I sat on the mat covered sand and began to open the packages. Mom had sent me a stack of communist newspapers and a letter, my sister Kathi a stash of tea and a letter, and Dad some razors I'd asked for, but no letter.

It was as if I'd been punched in the chest. I grabbed the stack of letters I'd received from home since arriving in country and counted them. Only one from Dad. I began to sob, hyperventilating, snot smearing my face. Crying jags had become routine for me since arriving in Gabi. Some days I had no idea what had triggered them, but today I did.

Dad was my anchor. After my parents divorced, I lived with him and visited Mom and Kathi on weekends. He was a hard-working man who wanted more than anything to raise independent and confident children. Living with him, I grew from a shy, insecure ten-year-old kid to an independent teenager who took college level Japanese evening classes and learned how to cook a *boeuf bourguignon* recipe to entertain his friends at dinner parties. His friendship helped me to survive.

When I began to breath normally again, I reached for the stack of photos of family and friends that I used to explain my life back home to villagers. I flipped through them and traced the faces with my finger. I was so far away. Every time I chose to hide who I was, to not tell them I was gay, to not live the truth, all collapsed into this one moment. Why had I run away from them? I would give the world to talk to all of them right then, to say that I loved them. But I had chosen to fortify my closet with walls 5,000 miles thick, made of sand and Acacia and ocean.

I put away the photos, stepped out of the room into the heat of the midday and almost ran into the young girl selling *kosai* millet fritters. I was so happy to see her that I bought four of the greasy things.

I sat down in the shade of my courtyard, pulled out some writing paper and began composing a letter to Dad. *I got your package*, I wrote, *but a letter would have helped a lot.* I tried not to sound passive aggressive or needy. I proceeded to apologize for leaving, which felt increasingly like a selfish act. I told him that I loved him. I had never done this before. Never had I told either of my parents I loved them, either in person or in writing. I insisted that I was doing fine, which was a complete lie. I needed more than anything to get his reassurance. But I didn't want him to worry. I folded the letter, shoved it in an envelope and mailed it on my next weekly mail run.

More weeks passed and I felt more comfortable in my Gabi. Amadou and I became friends. When I'd be sick in the latrine late at night, throwing up from Giardia, it was Amadou who called out asking if I was OK. Often, we'd sit in the courtyard of the house after I'd done my gardening and we'd talk. My Hausa language skills were finally to a point where I could talk about most things, but I couldn't yet express emotion. He told me that if I ever got really sick that he could take me on his mule cart to the nearest clinic in Bande, ten kilometers away through the thorn scrub and sand.

One afternoon as we stood in the compound, he put on my sunglasses, grabbed my folio where I kept important papers and went to stand by my *moto*.

"Take my picture," he said, as he posed smiling, pointing to my Nikon SLR.

I snapped a shot of him.

"Someday, I will come to America and live with you," he said with a laugh.

I tried to imagine Amadou surviving a subzero Minnesota winter. Would he do any better than I was at surviving I the Niger hot season? What did he think of me, the outsider, the comparatively rich, white American who could come to Africa? He, the African, who couldn't come to America without a visa and a significant amount of money to do so. I had wanted an authentic experience here, to live like the villagers around me, but my *motorcycle*, a *laisser-passez* card that enabled me to go wherever I wanted to, made me different.

"Maybe," I said, and laughed too.

I received Dad's reply exactly a month after I had sent it. A four-pager with photos and a book titled *Love*, by someone named Leo Buscaglia.

Now there's a real letter, he wrote, *I love you, too, very much.*

In my search for the meaning of life I've discovered that love is a key ingredient. It's necessary to love & to be loved. So I'll send you a Leo Busccaglia book which Trudy once sent to me.

I felt relief, then gratitude and finally stupidity. Why did I ever doubt that he loved me or that he wouldn't support me? I thought that it was the right time to tell him that I was gay. In fact, I felt an urgency to do so. I was 5,000 miles away, but I had to do it. A phone call was out of the question—talking from a phone booth at the post office, connecting through an international operator—I couldn't do it. But I could make him a tape so that way at least he'd hear my voice.

I picked up the book and read the back cover—Buscaglia was a motivational speaker on PBS, a proponent of self-love. In the first few pages he hypothesized that everyone needs to learn how to love. I flipped through the pages and continued to read like a hungry bird. It made perfect sense to me. I had never felt worthy of people's love. I had blocked out the world in those post-divorce years and learned to be self-sufficient. I had decided to come to Africa to sort out everything on my own. Only I was quickly learning that it was un-workable and that maybe I did need other people. Living the truth was the ultimate act of self-love.

That evening I sat down in my chair. The jaundiced light of my hurricane lamp spread around me, and I pulled out my Walkman inserted a cassette tape. Where to begin? *As you may have guessed*, or *little did you know*, or *obviously*. I felt ridiculous facing off to a tape recorder instead of person or a telephone receiver. But this was my only way. I recorded, backed up, recorded again, mumbled my words. Eventually I got something out that felt cohesive. It was as stressful as telling him in person, as though he was inside that Walkman. I immediately felt sick to my stomach, filthy. Nobody in my family had ever talked about gayness. I had grown up in the age of Anita Bryant. I had just thrown a label on myself and tried to imagine what my family thought of me with it on. I felt like I was standing naked on a mountain top, a strong wind beating down on me. I shut off the Walkman, pushed it aside, blew out the hurricane lamp and went to bed.

The next evening, I sat down in the same spot again, rewound the tape and hit play. Listening to the sound of my own voice was excruciating. I lit a cigarette and inhaled deeply. I was doing a chicken shit thing trying to pull this off from this distance. It would take weeks to get to him and I would wait more weeks for a reply. If he responded negatively, I had no support here—my closest volunteer friends were on the other side of the country. This self-imposed exile, which I thought was what I needed to figure out how to live the truth, was keeping me from doing just that. I realized there was no way I could send this tape. I took a sip of iodine purified water, rewound the tape one last time and pressed record. This time I recorded a mundane letter telling him about my successes in the garden and how hot it was getting. I put the Walkman away and lit another cigarette. I would have to leave here in order to come out.

The hot season turned to the rainy season. I could smell the moisture in the air. Every night the wind would pick up and a dust storm began, the precursor to rain, only the rain never came. Weeks went by. My garden grew bigger. My Hausa got better. But my ambivalence about being in Niger wasn't going away.

Four months after arriving in Gabi I attended a Peace Corps

In-Service Training in Niamey with other volunteers. Being around them, speaking English, made me feel better. But we all complained about our situations. Most of the others didn't have work either. I never thought to present my problems as more formidable than theirs. I was becoming disillusioned with the concept of Third World Development. What was it we were trying to accomplish here anyway? And, in addition to my gastro-intestinal woes I had developed a mysterious jaw pain that the Peace Corps doctor hadn't been able to explain or diagnose. I was becoming unhinged.

One night, after a serious discussion of our various predicaments, a more senior volunteer named Jay said, "It takes more courage to leave here than to stay." His words gave me pause. Courage to leave meant saying that this wasn't working, and I need to move on, whereas staying meant just enduring.

Early Termination. That's what the Peace Corps called it when you decide to leave early—ET for short. A clinical, precise and pejorative term. A sign of weakness by other volunteers, although we'd all fantasized about it.

The morning after I returned to Gabi, I walked to my garden and sat down on the log overlooking my own Walden Pond. The new humidity in the air reminded me that the rains were coming. A Fulani herdsman walked by singing a forlorn song and thwacking his goats. Jay's words were stuck in my head on repeat. Leaving would take courage, courage to face the life ahead of me. Courage that I didn't know if I had. Staying would take a resiliency that I didn't know if I had either. I thought to myself how lucky Gabi was compared to other villages in Niger. They had the ability to farm year-round. They had a well, a pump, a tree nursery, a millet grinder and now emergency shipments of millet from the US government. They didn't need me, the privileged, helpless Peace Corps volunteer who got lost every time he left the village. Everything I did or thought I could do was being done better by someone else. If I could switch places with any of the villagers, I wouldn't survive long without my filtered water, malaria pills or my *moto*. But if I had to leave in the morning Gabi would be just fine. But would I be OK without Gabi?

What I thought my African sojourn would give me—isolation and perspective—only distanced me and made it harder to do what I needed to do: come out with the support of my family. There was no way I could live the truth while I was here. As much as I wanted to be self-sufficient, I needed other people. The door to this room I'd locked myself into was wide open and I was ready to walk out of it.

The next week I sat sweating on the seat of a cross-country bus for the twelve-hour ride to Niamey along Route 1, speeding over the tarmac and through heat mirages. I was going to demand that the Peace Corps figure out what was going on with my jaw. If they couldn't, maybe they would Medivac me to the States for a diagnosis. If they wouldn't Medivac me, I decided, then I would ET.

Check.

As in a game of chess, I moved closer to my closing move.

"There is nothing wrong with your jaw that I can find," the Peace Corps doctor told me after days of testing. "We wouldn't Medivac unless we knew what was wrong with you."

Check mate.

The next morning, I woke at the Peace Corps hostel with the clarity of what I needed to do ringing like church bells on a Sunday morning. I showered and took a taxi to the Peace Corps office.

"I want to ET," I blurted to David, the country director.

I felt like I was having an out-of-body experience. As if a different person were making these decisions and acting on my behalf. I was no longer the hapless volunteer sitting in his village. I knew what I needed to do.

"Why?" he asked.

The reasons spilled out of my mouth—chronic illness, boredom, heat, anxiety, depression. The biggest reason—that I couldn't live the truth here in a country where my kind were illegal—I kept guarded. I flashed to the *Don't Ask, Don't Tell* moment during Stateside training and decided that the Peace Corps didn't deserve to know.

"But you've got so much potential," he added, "Are you sure there is nothing I can do to convince you to stay?"

"No," I said, "I need to return to Gabi to get my things first and say goodbye to the villagers."

"That isn't possible," he said, "we'll need to get you on the next flight out."

The reality hit me like a cross-country bus. I couldn't return to Gabi to say goodbye to the villagers. I would never see them again and probably none of my Peace Corps friends either. I was furious.

I got up to leave the office.

"You can ask another volunteer to pack one duffel with your things," he added as I walked out of the office, "we'll ship it home to you surface freight."

I flew back to the US and spent the summer in St. Paul living with Dad, doing odd jobs to save money for a move to Seattle. He was happy to have me, and it felt natural moving back in to his home. Coming out to him, however, seemed less urgent now than it had in Niger. I was busy preparing for my new life on the West Coast.

In late August, I drove across the country. Arriving in Seattle at sunset, I watched the sky over the Olympic Mountains turn from gold to crimson, and I knew I had found my new home. I moved into a studio on Belmont Avenue in Seattle's Capitol Hill neighborhood, across from a gay bookstore called Beyond the Closet.

I went on dates. There seemed to be a gay man on every corner and in every Starbucks. The possibilities seemed endless.

Then one date turned to several, and I suddenly had a new boyfriend. It was time to tell Dad. I wrote him a letter and he called me as soon as he received it.

"I love you," he said when I answered the phone. He seemed calm, unbothered by the news, like he had been expecting it.

"I would have told you earlier, but..," I said. I didn't know what to add.

"It doesn't matter," he said. "All that matters is your happiness."

I had been stateside for almost half a year when the duffel from Niger caught up with me. I threw it on the studio floor and began pulling out my shortwave radio, cassette tapes of Kate Bush, Peter Gabriel and The Indigo Girls, and my old notebook of raw poetry. Everything smelled of the dust and heat of the Sahel, of the angst and fear I had left in Niger.

Cold Night in Waterloo

Robert Garner McBrearty

Somewhere out on this country road, Paul comes to, freezing. The cold is sobering him up fast now, and it wasn't a complete blackout this time, but he knows with regret that for the last few minutes he was functioning in that otherworldly state he knows too well, and damn, he blew a ride in a warm car with three guys and a girl he hooked up with in the honky-tonk bar just outside his cheap motel on the highway. They thought he was funny at first, all of them bump-dancing with their butts, and he thought the girl, skinny and dark-haired, with gleaming teeth, might be a little sweet on him, might be seriously thinking of dumping the duds she was with, which led him to make that stupid pass in the car at her when they invited him to go to a party outside of town. He has a fuzzy memory now, crammed up against her in the backseat, leaning in and blowing in her ear; had he really said, "Let's light it up, baby, let's light it up tonight, what do you say, you and me?" What the hell sort of thing was that to say to a girl? That was a stupid thing to say, like out of a bad movie.

At thirty, he seems to be doing that more and more, playing characters in bad movies. It's been one bad roll after another since getting out of the service. Holding himself, hugging himself, now using his hands to beat a little heat in around his chest—he's got a cheap parka, not worth a crap in this near zero weather—he remembers he didn't just whisper to her, he touched her thigh until he felt the warmth beneath her blue jeans. But then she blew a hard breath, grabbed his hand and threw it off her like something diseased, and yelled, "Oh God! He's *touching* me! Get him out! Get him out of the car!"

The driver pulled to the side of the road. "Get out, you

asshole." The guy in the back seat over against the other door reached past the girl to slug him, punching him over her shoulders so the punches were bouncing off his head, little dings that he could ignore, but then the other guy in the passenger seat got into it, too, turning around in the seat and punching at his forehead, more annoying dings, and he thought about kicking their asses and making off with the car and the girl.

But, politely, keeping his cool, he said, "Okay, okay, I'm going, fuck you all if you can't take a joke." Out he went and they peeled off, and here he is in the dark, freezing his ass, his cell phone dead, forgot to charge the goddamn battery. *Oh God! What did she mean by wailing out like that, like he was some kind of monster?*

What he needs right now, goddamn it, there it is. The one thing he needs most in the world is that farmhouse, that porch light shining back from the road a hundred yards ahead and down a long gravel driveway. He's going there. People who live in places like that, maybe not even working farms, but a little land, grow a few tomatoes or something, those people are the salt of the earth, read the bible, don't turn out the stranger in your midst. Won't let a guy freeze.

Not another place in sight. Pickup truck in the driveway. Solid folk, kindly people.

He walks up the wooden steps of the porch, off to the left, a swinging bench—*salt of the earth!* He pauses a moment in the yellow porch light of the old white house with the chipped siding. Knocks. Knocks louder, hugging himself. He's got to get in. He's got to get out of the cold. He's not dying out here. Nobody's dying tonight, not happening, not on my watch.

A dog, a fierce brute from the sound, letting loose inside. He likes dogs, but this pup doesn't sound friendly. A door opening, stopped by a chain lock, and an old man peering through the crack. The dog, a German-Shepherd, barking to kill. The old man swats at the dog. "Shut up, Claude." The dog whines, but he's pushing his nose past the man's leg. "What do you want?"

Paul hears noise, people talking in the background. That could be good. Old guy will be less afraid if he's not alone. But the sound changes and he realizes it's only noise from the television set back in another room.

"My car broke down. A mile from here, a couple of miles from here, I've been walking. I'm sorry to bother you, mister. I'm freezing out here. It's cold as…it's cold."

The old man's eyes glint behind the glasses, sharp little eyes, and the thin white eyebrows give the old bird a harsh sort of look. "Why are you out on this road? Where are you from?"

"I'm just passing through. I was trying to get to this party."

"A party? There's no party out here, son."

"Yeah, well, it was all kind of a big misunderstanding. I'm just trying to get back to town. I got a motel room there."

The old man nods slowly. "I'll call somebody for you. You give me a number to call."

"I'm not from around here. I don't have anyone to call." One good kick might break that chain, drive the door in, but there's the dog. It bares its teeth and growls before the old man swats him again. "Shut up, Claude. That's enough. I'm trying to talk to the man here."

'Trying to talk to the man here' sounds good, willing to work with a guy, salt of the earth. If he does kick in the door, the man might take it the wrong way, will think he'll hurt him, when he just needs to get out of the cold.

"Tell you what, son, I'm going to call the sheriff to come by and give you a lift to town. He lives just a couple of miles from here, or he'll send the deputy. Won't take long." The old man says *sheriff* and *deputy* in a way he knows will drive him off.

Paul stares at him through the crack. "Never mind, mister. I'm moving on. I'll just freeze to fucking death out here. You remember that." He falls backs from the door as if tugged away and heads back down the gravel driveway, but once out of the circle of light cast by the porch light, he's in the darkness. And there's the pick-up truck in the driveway. He's hot-wired cars a couple of times, but he wasn't that good at it, and that was in the light. In the dark, with his frozen hands, that's not going to work. There's a shed. He could hide out in that, pull some sacks over himself or something. But the shed's padlocked.

There's that barking again, but louder. The old man might turn the killer dog loose to make sure he clears out of here. Let a guy freeze out here, ought to die on his doorstep, make him happy. He's never imagined how great a cheap motel room could be, just the warmth of that room would just be so great right now. Why did he get in this fix, all over a girl who had the best teeth in the world? He can see that smile now, it lit up that barroom. She probably did have a thing for him. He just moved a little too fast.

They don't usually lock the windows in these old farmhouses. He picks a window in the back, in the far corner of the house. The piled-up snow gives him a good cushion, raises him to the right level. Perfect, not even a screen. Sure enough, the window jams up, then releases. He pushes the window higher, gives a hop, lies sprawled in the frame. He drops into a dark room. He crawls his way along a carpeted floor. The old man cries out from the front door, "Claude! Claude! Come back here, you stupid dog!"

Claude's clueless. His barking recedes into the distance, down the country road, maybe out on a long romp after some dog buddy or girl. Good to get old Claude out of the picture. Paul lies on the floor, breathing. Okay, he knows this scene. Scenes like it. Plenty of dark houses he's gone into. But that's with a flashlight, though you didn't want to use it much, as little as possible. But not houses with people inside. At least not intentionally, though he'd been surprised a couple of times. Now he's got an old guy loose in the house somewhere. He doesn't think there's anybody else. The guy's too old to have kids living with him, and if there was a wife, he'd have heard something from her by now. He could just bed down in this room, just stay on the floor, but that's risky. Doesn't know if the old man is going to get suspicious and prowl around. The old buzzard might have already called the cops. But he can't head back out to freeze. The keys. Okay, he's got to find the keys to the truck and get out of here fast. He remembers that on the drive with the three losers and the girl with the gleaming teeth—*maybe it wasn't too late, he'd find that party and pull up in the truck and off they'd go*—they'd passed branch roads. Avoid the cops, who'd be thinking he was some sort of dumbshit who'd panic and head for the highway. Hit those back roads instead and work his way around to the motel, exchange the old truck for his own car and get out of town. They'll be looking for the truck, not his old beater. He can still get out of this one.

But find those keys. Find those keys fast. He rises to his feet. Creeps down a hallway, eyes adjusting now. *Remember your strengths! This is what you're good at! You are very damn good at this! Then why have I always hit half-ass houses, why not a high-rise now and then? I'm getting out of it, I'm getting out of the field, the field's moved on. I didn't want to do this. This is the last time ...* He moves toward the light of the den. He hears the TV again and the old man is probably sitting there watching *Hawaii Five-O*, probably never called the cops at all. Maybe I'll just walk right in and say give me the fucking keys. No, be nice, don't give him a stroke.

Sure, he knows how these houses work. These rooms off the hallway are where the kids used to live, but they're empty now. Then there'll be a little living room, off to the right the front door, to the left a den with the TV—probably some old TV with a yellow screen, hardly worth ten bucks at a pawn shop. Another room off the living room where the old man sleeps. Lonely old guy. Wife probably died. Should say something consoling to him. His own mom had died, dad too, they were good people. He hated it when people blamed their parents for how they turned out. *His parents had been good people! He wouldn't have anybody speaking out against them!* The TV turns off suddenly. That could be good, old guy going to bed. He freezes in the hallway, listens. Okay, go, easy.

Into the living room now, keys probably hung up right by the front door. Yes, that's where he'd keep them, that's where they always keep them in farmhouses. *Salt of the earth!*

Crossing the hardwood floor toward the keys, his heart lurches and he halts abruptly. The old guy is standing behind an armchair staring right at him, and what is worse, a whole hell of a lot worse, is that the old man is aiming a shotgun right at his chest.

"Stop right there," the old man says.

"Okay," Paul says. "Okay. Don't shoot. I don't mean any harm."

He goes all weak inside, legs trembly. Nothing worse than a shotgun at close range. Looks like he knows how to use it, too. Probably some old Marine. That gun will blow him in two if the man's finger goes all twitchy.

The chair is a nice touch. A good smart touch. Keeps him from lunging at the old man, if he even wanted to.

"You stand right there."

"Yes, sir."

The old man squints. "No. Sit on the floor."

He starts to obey, then shakes his head. "No."

Louder now, a wag of the gun, but a waver in the man's voice. "Sit on the floor."

He had to know this. He knows now the old man won't shoot easily.

"I'm going to leave. I'm going to walk out the front door."

"Don't move."

"I'll walk out of here. You don't want to shoot a man in the back. The cops will pick me up."

He sees something change in the man's face. Maybe the old guy hasn't called the cops after all, maybe heard a noise and picked up the shotgun first.

"Okay. Go ahead and walk out of here."

"I wasn't going to hurt you. I'm not that sort of person."

"I don't care what kind of person you are. Just get out."

"Okay. "

He opens the door, gets hit with the blast of the cold wind. Claude charges up the lawn, barking and growling and flashing his teeth. He slams the door shut and twists the doorknob lock as if Claude might burst right through.

He turns around. "You've got to call off your dog."

The old man hesitates, wags the gun again. "All right, move aside."

The man comes carefully out from behind the armchair. Some faint noise from a side room makes him turn his head a notch. Paul's fast. He jumps forward, grabs hold of the barrel. Using it for leverage, he drives the man back across the room, tears the gun from his hands, and pushes him into the armchair where the old man sits and looks in wide-eyed terror at the shotgun aimed at his face.

Paul hears it now, a sound almost disappearing under the sound of Claude barking outside the front door. A baby whimpering in the other room, only partly crying, as if the baby hasn't fully woken up.

He lifts his eyebrows. "What's going on? Who's that?"

"My granddaughter. I'm the babysitter tonight. The kids went to a movie. They'll be back soon."

The baby gets a little louder, but the sound is still muffled, coming and going.

"What do you need to do?"

"Let's leave her out of this. Please."

Paul stares at him. "You think I'd hurt a baby?"

"You've got that shotgun, son. Stop waving it around."

"Get her back to sleep. We don't need a crying baby here." He walks behind the man, following with the shotgun, but keeping it aimed down at the floor. A nightlight in the room casts a yellow glow on a rickety-looking old crib. The old man swoops the baby gently up, soothes her on his shoulder. Her whimpering grows louder.

"She needs a bottle," the old man says. "Go to the kitchen. Get a bottle out of the fridge. It's all made up."

"Oh, Jesus."

"Do it if you don't want her screaming."

"My God. I wish I'd never knocked on your fucking door."

"I never asked you to. Watch your language. The baby."

"Yeah, yeah, okay. Sorry. I'm not around babies that much."

He goes into the kitchen, gets out the bottle and brings it to the old man who is now sitting back in the armchair holding the baby. He gives the old man the bottle and stands back, keeping an eye on them but holding the barrel of the shotgun away, aimed down at the floor. He watches in a kind of amazement as the baby pulls at the bottle with greedy little lips. He'd had a girlfriend once who'd wanted a baby. Maybe he ought to go back and look her up. She wasn't too far from here. Nebraska. Maybe she'd be happy to see him. Wouldn't that be something, if she opened the door and smiled, happy to see him. She'd had little gaps between her front teeth. But they were pretty gaps, he was okay with them. He had a thing about teeth. That girl in the bar had had great teeth.

By degrees the baby settles. The old man gets up slowly and carefully and he lays her back down in the crib, and they go back into the living room.

"Sit back down in the chair," Paul says.

"Take the keys to the truck. They're on the ring there, right where you were heading."

"You must think I'm a bad person."

The old man shakes his head. "No. Sometimes people end up in a bad way without knowing how to they got there. But they can turn it around."

"All I wanted was to get out of the cold. It was all because of a girl. I liked this girl."

"Take the keys and go, son."

"I don't go around hurting people. I wasn't raised that way."

"I believe you."

"I'll go now. I don't even want your damn truck. Just call that dog off."

Headlights come from the driveway, shine through the front curtains. He looks at the old man, who takes a fast breath. "It's my son and daughter-in-law, coming for the baby. Please don't do anything to them. I won't say anything."

He looks at the old man. "We already had this conversation. I'm not like that."

Now a knocking on the door, movement of the knob, someone pushing against the door. More knocking.

"Get the baby," Paul says.

"Please."

His hands shake on the shotgun. "Get the goddamn baby."

The man makes a frightened sound in his throat, but he goes in to get the baby. When he comes out with her, Paul says, "Wrap her up good. It's cold out there. Take the baby and clear out of here."

The old man turns at the door, baby cradled in the blanket against his shoulder. "Turn yourself in, son. I'll spin it the best way I can." He pauses. "I would have let you in if it hadn't been for the baby. My son wouldn't forgive me for letting in a stranger. I would have let you in. I want you to know that."

"I don't give a damn. Just go."

The old man opens the door part-way, wedges past the snarling dog as his son from the front porch says, "What the hell, Dad?"

"Go to the car, Jim."

"Dad? What's going on?"

"Walk, Jim, walk. Claude, move your ass!"

Paul locks the door behind them. He sits in the armchair, holding the gun across his lap, more tired than he's ever felt in his life. But not cold. He'll just sit here in the warmth and wait. The old man probably *would* have let him in. *Salt of the earth.* He wishes now he'd told him he believed him. He should have at least given the old man that, after all the trouble he's caused. The funny thing is, he kind of liked the old man. On a better night, he'd have had a beer with him and sat on the couch watching television while the old man talked about missing his wife, and he'd talk about missing his parents, and maybe they'd remember some old iron-assed sergeants who'd helped them keep their heads on straight. Before long, the lights, more than one car now, shine through the front window, the cop lights spinning in the driveway and the yard, casting an eerie strobe light through the house, checkering, pulsing across the walls, and he hears static from their cop radios. *Why is there always static? Who is there to call? How many does it take?* He moves to the window, pulls the curtain back, stands there in the frame, holding the shotgun but not aiming it, waiting for the next move. *Good country cops, salt of the earth!* He thinks about busting out the glass, but it seems sort of dramatic, like a scene in a bad movie. Maybe he could drop back out that back window and make it across a field. Sure, get across a field, find a country road, hitch a ride, maybe say: *hey, I heard there was a party somewhere out here, you going there?*

A Degenerate Gambler's Report

Suzanne Heagy

They say what happens at Bittinger's, stays at Bittinger's. It's out in the hollow on the county line, where even the Guv'ner can't get an Uber. We yokels are known to each other, but we're not averse to a stranger. Last weekend, I was in the game room gambling and losing fifty cents every spin. Bittinger's has six video gambling machines—three Game Kings, two penny machines, and a flashy new machine with keno games I'd not seen before. That machine ate my last ten-dollar bill without giving a whistle or ringing a bell. I moved over to my favorite, number one, an old Game King in the corner, and fed it my last eight dollars.

Into the game room walks this couple I haven't seen before. I look them over without being obvious. She's tall, willowy, with wild brunette hair in one of those messy buns, maybe thirty years old, and way too easy on the eyes for the fellow who's with her. He's two inches shorter, no neck to speak of, with a muttonchop face, square wire-rimmed glasses, and a John Deere cap on his noggin.

She sits down at one of the penny machines and looks at the games. She says, "Oh, I've played Buffalos before."

The guy sits down at the machine beside her and spins his chair in her direction. He pulls a twenty out of his wallet and forks it over. "Here ya go, honey. Lock it up."

She looks at the money and then at him. She says, "Aren't you going to play?"

He says, "I'm happy just to sit here and watch."

The brunette hands his twenty back. "If you're not gambling, I'm not gambling. It's a two-way street."

"Okay," the guy says and pulls another 20 out of his wallet

and puts it in the machine where he sits, number four, another Game King.

She must have been max betting on Buffalos because it's not five minutes before she says, "That's it. I lost."

The guy has hardly been spinning at all. He says, "I'll just cash out."

"Oh, no," she says. "I got a feeling you're gonna' get lucky tonight. You keep playing, hon. I'll be at the bar." And she stands up and saunters out with her beer.

The guy slumps in his chair and stares into number four's screen.

I'm playing ten numbers on Caveman Keno, only betting a quarter, random picking my numbers every three spins, and suddenly I hit seven out of ten to win twenty-four bucks. I could cash it out, having tripled my money, or keep playing and try for more.

The guy next to me makes up his mind and hits the "Cash Out" button, takes his ticket, and goes back in the bar.

Sometimes when the machine's teasing me, I can play on twenty bucks for an hour. Win a little, lose a little, back and forth. I kept playing and was down to less than a dollar when I hit for ten to bring me back up.

Kelsey, who is loud, stacked, and proud, came flouncing into the game room. She stopped right next to me and crossed her arms. "You have to come out to the bar. There's some woman rubbing on Calvin, and I don't like it."

I trusted Calvin like I trusted my right hand. "It's fine," I said. "Let the old man have a thrill." Maybe if Calvin got roused up, I'd benefit later at home.

"I don't like it. I'll take care of it for you."

"Don't stir up any trouble, please." Kelsey once tipped a biker bitch off a bar stool and almost caused a war.

"I'm just going to stand in between them."

"You do that," I said. Calvin would like it. He thought Kelsey was a hoot.

I tried picking five numbers and sticking with them, but that strategy wasn't getting me anywhere. I went back to ten numbers and random picks and played down to fifteen cents. I switched to my favorite spin game, Lionfish, and played my last three credits. Bust. I didn't hit a thing.

Calvin would cover my bar tab, but he hardly ever gave me gambling money because one of us had to have some sense. I went out to bar so he could buy me a beer, liquid consolation.

He was sitting by himself on a barstool. I could see Kelsey hanging out with the pool table crew in the back. The brunette and her man were nowhere in sight. I slid onto the stool next to Calvin.

"I don't see a ticket," he said.

"I guess it's not my lucky night." I said to Brandon, who was bartending, "Bring me a Miller Lite, please."

He went to get it, and I turned to Calvin. "I hear you had an admirer. Where'd she go?"

Calvin wasn't really my husband, but he might as well have been. He spent the night at my place on my thirtieth birthday and hadn't ever left. He always quoted the Glen Campbell song and said his sleeping bag was rolled up behind my couch.

"They left," he said. "Her and the guy who was with her. I think they were on a date."

"I think she was trying to ditch him," I said. "What did you two talk about?"

"Nothing much." My man looked at me. "Do you want to gamble some more? I have twenty dollars, if you want to try again."

Calvin always knew how to perk me up. "I wouldn't mind," I said.

Bittinger's door opened, and the strange man walked back in. His physique looked like somebody sat a cinder block on his head and pushed down until his neck collapsed.

He came over to where we were sitting. "Hey," he said, "you know that woman I was with? Have you seen her come back in?"

"Nope," I said.

Calvin gave me a twenty. "I thought she walked out with you."

"She did," the guy said. "We were to the truck, and then she said she forgot something. I waited with the motor running, but she never came back. I don't know where she got off to."

I looked at Calvin. There was nowhere to get off to around Bittinger's. The nearest house was a mile away, and the gas station was two miles further. "Maybe she's in the bathroom," I said. "Let me check."

I went to the lady's room, and the door was unlocked. I used the toilet and washed my hands. I went back out. "Nope, she's not in there. Sorry, buddy, I haven't seen her."

The man looked back and forth between us. "She's been staying at my house. What should I do with her clothes?"

"She'll be back to collect 'em," I said. "Give her a few days."

The man shook his head. "I don't think she's coming back."

Calvin looked at me. He said, "You going to gamble or not? I'm ready to leave after this beer."

"Okay, okay," I said, standing to head back to the game room.

"What should I do?" the guy asked.

"Drive slow on your way back to town," Calvin advised. "If she's headed home, you'll run into her walking."

Back in the game room, I looked at the machines and tried to divine which one felt lucky. I felt drawn to the penny machine that the brunette had played. For a second, I wondered what could have happened to her. Then my gambling itch took over, and I sat down and slid the twenty in to play.

Phantom Power

Ulrick Casimir

Manuel's no-show job kept him eight to five down at Carson Cement, so it was Linda's responsibility to have the house cleaned, and dinner fixed, and the recliner angled right, and the remotes in clear sight, and Manuel's drink—a screwdriver with a mandarin/key-lime mixture made from scratch—ready for the man the moment he got home from work.

She had always kept a clean home, so that part was simple. Tidying, some picking up. A bit of careful dusting, making sure the rag she used on the borders of the flat-screen didn't leave another expensive, injurious scratch on the face of it. She had to close the curtains, too, because it was part of what he wanted, how he liked things. Dinner was potatoes, mashed or roasted with onions, olive oil, rosemary. The beans Manny liked came out of a can, but the meat—steak or chops, depending on the sale at Ray's—*had* to be cooked over charcoal, in that little grill by their back door. The recliner was simple … or simpl*er*, ever since Linda started marking the angle he liked best with a felt-tip pen that barely showed, a mark only she could see. The remotes, too, were easy.

It was the drink that took longest and had her panicked now. They lived in an old Levittown ranch, the 50th block of Alan Avenue. It was 5:00 p.m., and through their living room window stretched the Tehachapi Mountains and wind farms to the east, the shuttered women's prison to the west. On that clear spring afternoon, Linda pulled the curtains shut, thinking solely of her husband, what he liked and wanted.

Five minutes later the house was ready, dinner cooking, recliner and remotes ready to go. She went to make the drink then realized she'd forgotten to stop by Ray's on her way back from meeting Tommy at Haversack's, to pick up the oranges she *should've* picked up when she'd said she was going to, which was this morning. One orange left, a can of juice, a half-finished pint of lemonade: She would have to fudge the mix, and pray he'd be too high to note the difference.

By ten-past, she was squeezing the halved orange with one hand and measuring out the vodka with the other. There were key limes, at least. Linda quartered one, squeezed it into an ice-filled tumbler and added vodka, juice, mint. She finished at 5:12, two minutes late. Rather, *he* was two minutes late, and while this was abnormal, she was grateful for it.

Linda could feel the pork sizzling out back. She could smell the potatoes steaming, drying out in the oven. The house was empty and quiet and dark, and although she could not explain this sensation, she felt the danger threaded through this place, like the movement one feels in a bound-up spring. She checked the oven thrice, turned it down, reset the timer. She went out back to flip the chops and stoke the briquettes. She went back inside and straightened cushions, then drew drapes until they covered the windows perfectly, until the light outside pushed at them like air at the skin of a balloon. Twenty-past came and went, and her husband was now later than she'd ever known him to be ... and the more time passed the less relieved she felt, the heavier with dread the air in that house became. At twenty-three after, she could stand it no longer. Linda went to check the mail.

Bills. An Easter card from Manuel's mother. Credit offers, which Manuel always forbade her to open, which he'd instructed her to immediately toss into the grill. She took the junk mail out back, burned it—and suddenly there it was, that feeling again. Grief, worry ... relief? Maybe, she thought, he'd had an accident. Maybe his motorcycle had been sideswiped and the bastard was face down in the culvert by Highway 58. Maybe, just maybe, he'd still be there tonight, *late* tonight, crying out for help, mewling like a little baby girl making nothing but tiny, soundless bubbles in the mud, until she remembered that her cell was on vibrate and in her purse.

One call and a voicemail, both from Allie, Manuel's fat sister, a former prostitute who lived with her kids outside of Reno. They'd never met but Linda had seen Manuel's pictures of her, and she'd spoken with Allie by phone on the holidays. She knew Allie mostly through Manuel's complaints about her: those stories from when his sister had been addicted to *everything*. It had always bothered Linda that Allie didn't even bother driving down from Reno to the courthouse for the wedding. She'd always thought Allie hated her. This phone call was a surprise.

Linda poked at the screen of her phone and immediately heard a voice that reminded her of Manuel at his angriest…except this voice was higher pitched, and it sounded as if Allie had run upstairs to make the call. "Linda," she said, kids screaming in the background, "Allie here. Manny's sister, he called today. Piss-drunker than I ever heard him before. I shouldn't be telling you this, but I guess I'm calling because something is up with him, and maybe you, too, or maybe the both of you? He's my brother. I can smell it." And that was it.

The phone had buzzed twice in Linda's hand as she listened to the voicemail. A couple swipes and she saw the reason for it: two texts from Tommy. "He knows," read one. "RUN!" screamed the other, and Linda's vision instantly blued. She reached behind her for the wall there, felt it. Her sight began to clear, her heart began to slow. She put the phone in her pocket and began to run.

She grabbed her wallet and keys from a corduroy jacket from the living-room closet. Pall Malls and a pack of matches, shimmied into Manuel's Chico State hoodie—his favorite—then bolted out front without shutting off the grill or the oven. Five minutes later, she'd covered the two miles to Haversack's, the bar off Highway 58 where Tommy Schleeman tended Tuesday through Saturday, noon to close.

The place was a glorified doublewide on a makeshift foundation, converted over the years into something just solid enough to pass muster with the city. Linda parked her Dart down the street, around the corner from the bar's gravel lot. She grabbed her things from the passenger seat, dropped her cell into the console, and left the car running. She walked around to the rear of the bar, where Tommy parked.

His was a Monte Carlo from the early 1970s, gray with a half-rotted cloth top and a busted lock on the passenger side. Linda slid into it and felt at the bottom of the dash for the ledge where Tommy stashed his spare. The bar's jukebox was going, Miranda Lambert's "Kerosene" cranked up nice and hot: She could be crashing around in a Sherman tank out here, and no one inside would know it.

She started Tommy's car, saw the gas gauge at half…which he'd told her, more than once, meant there was actually just a quarter-tank left. But that was enough to get her to Bakersfield. She pulled the shifter down, nudged the vehicle to the road, eased onto her side of the highway, then punched the accelerator hard as she reached for her purse and counted the money it contained.

In Bakersfield, Linda slowed, cut across to Ment Avenue, to the Chase branch there, left Tommy's ride running as she cinched her hood tight and went to the ATM. He'd always kept a firm eye on the cash, Manny did, and he wouldn't let her work, so for years Linda had tried to be frugal with whatever funds he saw fit to dole out weekly, for groceries and such. She would spend as little as possible then put the rest in an account, one she'd started the day after the wedding, her own little secret. But three years of this had netted only $200.75.

She had a debit card, but she also knew enough not to use it. He'd gone to school with half the tellers here, he would find her in a minute if she used it. So it was the ATM, even though that meant leaving those precious, hard-earned quarters behind. She added the $200 to the $31.55 already in her purse and drove down to fill up at the Stop 'n' Sip outside of town.

Manny had never been north of San Francisco in his life. At the junction for Interstate 5, with $179 and little else in her purse, Linda made her first deliberate decision since Allie's voicemail and went north, didn't stop until she hit Sacramento and had to, for gas and the toilet. Filling up at the Valero there was another $55, leaving her $124 in cash.

Tommy kept a half-full bottle of Desoxyn in his dash; they were there, he'd told her late one night when Manny was off in L.A. working his real job, so whenever Tommy took a smoke break during a double, he could pop some to smooth out those fourteen-hour shifts. Inside the Valero, Linda spent another $4.00, this time on snacks and pop. She swallowed three Desoxyn in a single gulp then hit the highway again, due north, leaving Sacramento behind with no real idea how far those pills, or her cash, would take her.

Around 2:00 a.m., she reached Yreka. The only open place in that silent town where Linda could refuel was a truck stop, a T/A with a couple small islands for regular cars out front. The true trucker's part was out back: two rows of diesel filling stations with sixteen nozzles each, and a huge parking lot with oversized spaces where worn-out long haulers could stop and recharge.

It was a hot and sticky night, unusual for late spring that far north. Because she knew what it did to the mileage of her own car, Linda had resisted the urge to use the Monte Carlo's AC—the one accessory that Tommy had always made sure kept working. She'd long since dumped Manny's hoodie, and although she didn't realize this, the skintight tank top she'd been wearing all day was now fused with sweat to her body. And then she saw herself in the eyes of the trucker at the back of the store, the one screwing her with his gaze, up and down, through the open door of the beer cooler.

He was balding yet had a long, gray ponytail. He wore a black T-shirt advertising a Volvo dealership in Nevada, a brown woven-leather belt, and a silver signet ring with a bright red cross on it. He had a paunch, too, that seemed his main source of propulsion. She could hear the store's PA: "Trucking," by the Dead, and she watched this man waddle to the music as he closed the door of the cooler and began strutting like a peacock, cutting the space between them degree by degree.

And Linda let him. She weighed the $57.75 that she had just spent on gas, the $62.25 she still had left, the hunger that had been needling her since Sacramento; she thought of how hard and fast she'd been running, how she still didn't know when and where she would stop; she thought of the fact that her period would begin soon, that she'd need to buy something for it any time now, and she let that man come up to her, buy her beer, feed her, and lead her out back to his big rig, parked there like a beast asleep in a den with many other beasts. And when they were done, when he finished, she had another $100 in her pocket.

She also had a destination—his suggestion, the trucker's, based on a story his mother had told him long ago, about an aunt who'd had to get away in the 1970s and disappear, fast. She took half his case of beer with her back to Tommy's car.

Linda chewed then swallowed eight more Desoxyn at once, chased them with a lukewarm Bud, then started driving again. She stopped and did it all once more, at a Flying-J near Grants Pass: this time with a lean and brutal cuss, who banged her head into the steering wheel and ripped off a chunk of her hair before paying her $25 less than they'd originally agreed.

At eight in the morning, Linda groaned through the outskirts of Eugene and into the parking lot of a Motel 6 with rooms available at $35 a night. The clerk, a thin woman with pockmarked cheeks and teeth that looked brushed with battery acid, smiled the best she could and let Linda check in early.

Sixteen hours straight Linda slept, each hour feeling like the death of days.

A recovering meth addict who'd been given enough second chances to feel that she ought to pay it forward, the clerk, Sadie, held off the maids and let the sorriest, most desperate look-ing guest she'd ever seen sleep three hours past checkout. When Linda finally woke, cleaned up, and went to pay, Sadie covered half the balance herself and gave the poor woman one of the motel's business cards, with the name, address, and phone num-ber of the Eugene Mission scrawled on back.

When Linda got to the mission and saw herself in the mirror behind the receptionist, she remembered the sorry way that clerk had looked at her. She looked a mess but the mission staff passed zero judgments, asked no searching questions. They seemed to pride themselves on this approach, so Linda let them.

They asked about drugs, kids, religion, whether Linda was a vegetarian or vegan, her preference for top or bottom bunk, and any issues sleeping in the dark. They asked if she needed a locker, or had a bag that needed stowing, if she was pregnant or if there were any gynecological services she might require. They showed her the chapel, the cafeteria, the beds, the barber, the laundry. Three free days, they said, then $2.00 a day, and she could earn more than that with daily chores. Chapel was required, and the woman said this was set in stone. Linda thanked them all, took another shower. She changed into the pajamas the mission provided and then slept again, for another twelve hours.

Her dreams that night weren't dreams, but recollections of what she'd recently done. She'd tossed the plates of the Monte Carlo and left the car idling out back of the motel. She then used some of the remaining money for a cab. En route to the mission, she got the cabbie to stop at the bus station, next to a trash bin where she deposited her license and Social Security and Safeway cards, anything that might be used to identify her. Deborah was who she was now, Deborah Clark, the name of the manager listed on the front of the hotel's business card.

She'd made those truckers use rubbers; even the cuss had obliged, as if he'd been burned that way before. Who she was, who she had been, was something that she'd scrubbed off in the showers at the hotel and the mission, a rank skin that shed with hard scrubbing, trailing after itself as it spiraled into the drain.

Yet the next morning, when she woke to the chime for breakfast served, Deborah threw off her sheets and blankets and began clawing at the air above her, in fierce battle with some moist and enveloping phantom power: a choking thing that she could not see, drowning her in an ooze so thick that it took a while to realize that at some point during the night, she had let herself go and wet the bed.

There was a man whom Deborah had heard the staff call Sunrise, and at first, she'd thought it was a joke. Twice a week, each Wednesday and Saturday morning at 11:00, Sunrise would truck in beets, potatoes, squash and whatever else was in season, from the garden that the culinary students at the community college tended to year-round. He was a roly-poly guy, about two inches shorter and a full foot wider than Deborah. When Sunrise spoke, which wasn't often, he did it so softly that even those who knew him well had to lean in to listen. And when he walked, he shambled so hesitantly, so lazily, that Deborah suspected he was constantly stoned.

It took her a couple weeks to overhear his name, another couple more to casually (and secretively) ensure that she'd heard it right, and another three to finagle a way for them to meet privately, without anyone at the mission catching on. At first, the mission's emphasis on segregating its male and female guests had made her smile. But what had felt quaint now began to seem creepy and strange: Something else in life that was being forced upon her.

Across the hall, down from the mission's pantries and coolers, was the chapel. Services took place there every night, the biggest on Saturday nights and Sunday mornings. But the space was almost always empty from 10:00 to 11:30 a.m. on Saturdays, so Deborah, thinking of Sunrise and the chapel's location near the pantry, picked that timeslot for her personal conversations with God, or whomever.

The chapel was warmly lit, wood paneling running a foot down from the ceiling, mirroring the grain of the lectern and pews. At first, since she was only there to establish the cover of routine, Deborah would bring a notebook and pass the time by drawing faces and sketching the room. Cover for both him and her; cover for the day when she would reach out to this man who made her smile even when he wasn't around, whom she could hear grunting, groaning, as he unloaded box after box, food that he gave his time to deliver for the benefit of the hopeless and the addicted, the homeless and the poor.

Four Saturdays in, something changed. Deborah changed, or began to change: She started leaving the notebook in her locker, sitting in the pews, thinking about life, her life, the one she'd left behind. She thought of Manuel, how things had begun with him, what they'd turned into, how they'd ended. She thought of God too, and fate and will and circumstance, and poor Tommy Schleeman, who used to take her up to the wind farms to watch the stars late at night when Manuel was off in L.A. working, doing to other people what she was pretty sure he'd already done to Tommy. Tommy, who loved that stupid Monte Carlo more than anything, who'd never put his hands on a woman in a hurtful way in his life.

And then she began to wonder at Sunrise: She imagined his life, what he must be like outside the mission, away from his job. This kind man who looked like the sort of hippy who would keep a garden just to watch butterflies flit and flowers grow. They could keep a garden, Deborah thought. They could find an apartment together, maybe lease a plot on the edge of town, spend next year's growing season scratching in the dirt, digging through the grime that coated them, springing into one another's arms. By her seventh Saturday morning in the chapel, Deborah realized she'd started kneeling, and could not recall when this whole kneeling thing had begun.

Eight Saturdays in, she was there on her knees, eyes shut, hands stitched together in prayer—when she heard the sound of a body rising from a pew. She opened her eyes, turned to the right ... but the large circular figure with a backside like melted marshmallows was already headed back down the hall.

On the cushion next to Deborah was a small honeysuck-le-scented slip the size of a nametag, on which he'd written his name and number. And at the bottom was a single word, "Namaste," in cursive, festooned with daisies, lilies, fractals, sketched and painted in inks, oils, and watercolor—

He said, "I've been thinking about this all day, meeting you. Talking to you. Conversing with you." And though he delivered this in a whisper, the shape of the chapel sent his plosives and sibilants twisting through space, echoing in the room's many corners and recesses.

And she said, "Oh," blushed, looked him in the eye for a moment, then looked down again, this time at the gap between them—which, since neither had moved, seemed to be shrinking on its own. Ah, she thought, magnetism. "Quiet," Deborah whispered. "Aren't you afraid?"

Earlier that morning, while cleaning the women's bathroom, Deborah had, for the first time in a week, caught a glimpse of herself in a mirror. She remembered how she used to look, be-fore Manuel; she remembered the state she was in the day she got to the mission. At her wedding she was 5'5" and a curvy 135 pounds. Her auburn hair was long back then, down to the small of her back, with curls that flowed into one another like waves of light or communication.

She had bright blue eyes and fair skin, and freckles that migrated with each change in the angle of the sun. Toni, her bestie in Tehachapi, had wanted to conceal them the day of the wedding, but Linda had said no: Everyone who saw the pictures said those freckles added depth to who she was.

By the time she got to the mission, Linda had dropped 15 pounds in two days. The skin on her face was loose, and there were bruises on her neck and arms, some so deep they seemed implanted far beneath the surface of her skin. Her nails broken, her lips cracked and dry: She'd left a patch of that long auburn hair in the passenger side of a Continental long-hauler in Grants Pass.

But in the months since, Deborah had gained all the weight back and then some, the extra pounds a happy fat evenly dividing itself between her working bits. She looked curvy again, and though she tried to cover it up, she got the occasional disapproving look from the female staffers. She'd always been proud of her shape. She could try to hide that from men, but never from women.

When the bruises faded, Deborah went to the barber at the mission, a Mexican named Paolo who was training to be a stylist at the cosmetology school three blocks away. He gave her a cute bob, shortest cut of her adult life, and she quickly got into the habit of tucking it behind her ears, so the back of her head was always where she carried it most.

Deborah's lips healed quickly. About a month into her stay, Sherry, one of the mission's youngest staffers—a college student who'd gotten a DUI and started working there as community service—gave Deborah a brand-new tube in a shade of pink that said the young girl had a good eye…and Deborah, in turn, treasured the lipstick and used it sparingly. Since receiving his note, each Saturday morning before chapel, she'd pull out the lipstick and apply a bit of it at a time, daubing her lips with tissue until her lips alone seemed responsible for her renewed and resonant glow. She'd arch her back then, push out her breasts and backside then, deciding once again that she was starting to like what she saw.

So when she asked the man if he was afraid, and he moved even closer, close enough that she could feel his breathing, the warmth of his body radiating in tangible waves—when he put his hand on hers and she snapped her head toward him and looked at his face, *she knew*. Even before he replied to her question, *she knew*.

"No way," he answered. "I'm not afraid. Not even the tiniest little bit. Are you?"

That winter was colder, grayer, wetter than ever, and Deborah, who'd never before spent a winter in the Pacific Northwest, did all she could to make it through. She read as many books as she could afford to buy from the dollar bin at the downtown Smith Family. She snagged a beat-up acoustic in the lost and found at the mission, then sat about humming and strumming, picking up whatever she could from any of the few dozen of the mission's guests who played guitar, and string-by-string, chord-by-chord, Deborah began to learn how to play. When she and Sunrise got together, they went for walks in the rain, or picnicked in waterlogged forests, or sat for hours chatting in sodden parks and the fields near the buttes. He had an umbrella so large it shielded them together from the drops of rain that often fell but sometimes swirled up, from the wintery clouds that shielded the entire western part of the state: from the rays of the moon, the stars. Even, eventually, the sun.

They were dating. She developed a new gait, as if something dense had shifted from her shoulders, or simply fallen on its own and shattered in a million pieces on the mission floor. No one but the two involved knew the reason for it, but *everyone* noticed the change. Each Saturday after they first spoke, he would drop off another ornate note and disappear before anyone could see. And each Saturday evening they would meet a few blocks away, near the downtown library, and do whatever it was he'd promised earlier on his note.

His given name was indeed Sunrise, Sunrise Zimmerman, and he'd lived in Eugene all his life. His parents, both dead, two hippies who'd met at Haight-Ashbury in the 1960s and stayed through its wild decline, had moved to Eugene in the early 1980s, shortly before his birth. He was shy, introspective, but spoke louder and more freely with her than she'd ever seen him do with anyone else—and she in turn expressed herself with him like she hadn't with anyone in years, not Toni, not Tommy, and *definitely* not Manuel. She told him her real name was Lucinda Bunting, that she'd left her hometown of Yreka with nothing, running from an ex who'd liked to rip out her hair and bang her head into the steering wheel … and then she told him the truth about Manny and his *real* job, the contracts he carried out at night sometimes for the cartels in L.A. She said that she could never go back, and Sunrise comforted and caressed her as she spoke, accepting everything she told him without judgment.

He was a computer geek, and what he didn't know how to do, his cadre of fellow geeks, some local and some not, could readily accomplish. It was Sunrise, with the help of friends Alex and Matt (ApophisL7 and 3asygr3asy, respectively), who turned "Linda Starling" into "Deborah Clark," at least in the eyes of the government. By midwinter she had a birth certificate, a license, a passport, and a Social Security card, all brand new and bona fide, with her new name on them. Shortly afterward, in February, Deborah left the mission and moved in with Sunrise.

He lived off a feeder that led from the southbound side of the interstate to the community college about a half-mile down. His house was a cozy, fully carpeted three-bedroom with cream-colored siding. Sunrise was a "patient" (migraines): One of the bedrooms had fluorescent lights everywhere and functioned as a nursery, while the finished attic was bisected by black plastic sheeting, with lights and buckets of water and nutrients for growing indoors during winter. There was a big, well-tended backyard, too, with high fences along which he'd set up discreet plots for growing when the outdoor season came. It took a while, but Deborah began to think of it as medicine, even to welcome the haze that often hung upon him. She came to associate the scent of weed with coming home.

It took them three weeks to clear the adjustment period that most couples spend several months or even a year getting through. She learned that he *liked* to dust and vacuum, that he enjoyed doing his own laundry and folding his own clothes: that he liked making breakfast but enjoyed it when she made lunch. And he preferred beer, *not* cocktails. She taught him much about herself, too: how it was a bad idea to let her start complaining, since sometimes she didn't know when or how to stop; the degree to which she hated cleaning the bathroom, especially the tub and toilet, after a man; the way she liked being woken up for sex in the middle of the night, and how little she enjoyed being frisky first thing in the morning.

The first time they'd slept together was two weeks after his first note, but he'd never let her go down on him or get a good look at his private parts until *after* she'd moved in ... and when he did, she understood why: He'd had a partial orchiectomy in his teens after being diagnosed with testicular cancer, and while he explained this meant he couldn't have kids, he'd been lucky enough to be spared some of the other effects. He told her this ... and she looked at the scar, touched him there, wondered silently how much lower his testosterone must be because of it. Then she grabbed his head and kissed him, said that she loved him, all of him, every present and missing part. Promised him she'd do so forever.

They married that summer, mid-August. At the Eugene Rose Garden: Smallish ceremony, peopled with mission staffers and current and former residents, ministered by Trillium Starchild, a longtime friend of Sunrise's who'd become a minister online for the occasion.

Wearing a druid robe and silver rings on each finger, Trillium Starchild did an excellent job with a ceremony that both bride and groom knew was illegal.

She gave them everything they asked for: ID in the form of a driver's license, symptoms, history, all forms filled out in block letters to the best of her knowledge and ability. She had no job but Sunrise did, so she was covered insurance-wise. She did what they said, went to the desk when called, waited as long as they deemed necessary. When the women up front finally beckoned, and the one in charge walked her back, Linda smiled as if the elegantly coiffed physician's assistant next to her, the one getting paid and not doing the paying, was doing the whole world, especially Linda, the biggest of favors.

They took vitals. They measured her up and down and side to side, asked question after humiliating question, and she calmly and repeatedly relayed the difficult and graphic answers: no to the discharge, yes to the burning and tingling—a small spot like a welt from a tiny whip on the bottom-left flap of her labia ... and yes, she answered: yes, it was fucking painful.

He was a balding man whose patience and directness spoke to years of experience and levelheaded practice. She removed her skirt and underwear; he took a brief look and told her what he thought it looked like, what she'd thought it was in the first place. The doctor then explained what would happen next: the blood test and, if it came back with the result they suspected, the phone call from the Oregon Department of Human Services, who would register her as a carrier and request phone numbers of all recent partners. The doctor, as he recited this, was inhumanly calm, and Linda's eyes drifted up to his pate, where she imagined the deep gray luminescence of a rainy winter's day, and not the fluorescents hovering above them in the windowless room, as responsible for the gleam she saw there.

Eyes shut, she imagined the rain drizzling on the street outside, spiking the surface of the millrace like grains of sand sprinkled from the heavens. She convinced herself that those weren't raindrops but tears, ones she'd supplied—that there were actual tears falling from her eyes, streaming down her face and falling into the millrace, though she'd never known a time in her adult life when she'd been able to cry. She'd actually begun pushing at her tear ducts, heaving herself at whatever it was that was blocking them, wondering whether it was the smell of the office, the strawberry scent of disinfectant, that was responsible for her current inability to weep, for this delay in desired and richly deserved weeping—when she felt the warmth of the doctor's hand upon her own.

"Wait here," he said. "The nurse will return in a moment and draw your blood. We'll call you in three days with the lab results. Deborah," he said, looking at her ring, "you said you're married?"

"Yes, recently."

"Yes, and you don't think you got this from him?"

"No," she said, thinking of Sunrise, his limited sexual history. "Probably not," she said slowly, as if listening to herself saying it.

The doctor squeezed her hand: "Any reason for us to worry after your safety? Because he has to be informed. But there are many, many different ways—"

"No. My husband would *never* touch me, nothing like that. Please," she said, jerking her hand out from under his.

He grew tall and rigid, brushing at the pressed thighs of his trousers. He spun on his heels to the door, repeating that the nurse would be in shortly as he walked out. Linda left the clinic before anyone had the chance to draw her blood. She then took a bus downtown, where Sunrise was finalizing an afternoon delivery to a university co-op.

That night, she made his favorite meal: plank-grilled salmon with a wasabi-soy sauce, ginger-sugar marinade; risotto with portobello mushrooms; greens with sliced strawberries, grape tomatoes, drizzled with sweet balsamic vinaigrette. The risotto she made in two batches: one with regular butter, and one with enough of his medicated olive oil to make the dish potent without noticeably altering the taste.

For the forty-five minutes it took to cook the salmon, Linda stood under an umbrella in the rain, manipulating the temperature and ports of the grill while Sunrise worked upstairs on his most recent crop. Eight plants were flowering on the far side of the sheeting; she could smell them from where she stood out back, a good ten yards from the house. A deep and verdant scent. It surprised her to realize how much she would miss it.

They had a bottle of wine with dinner, a bright chardonnay from a vintner Sunrise went to high school with, whose winery was somewhere out in Veneta. She would miss this too, the gently bragging, name-dropping part of him. They ate, they drank, they were happy together. They made love, twice, no protection.

The wine and sex together amplified his risotto: By 8:30 that evening, Sunrise was out cold, with one fat white leg sticking out from under the covers. When he started snoring, Linda rose, got dressed, grabbed some essentials from the dresser and closet and bathroom, threw them all into a duffel bag, and left the bedroom without once looking back at him.

She took his keys and his wallet, threw her stuff in the passenger seat of his van, and then went back into the house, to the cabinet under the sink in the laundry room. She took out the jumbo-sized bottle of bleach there and poured a cup into the soil of each and every plant in the house, the ones that were flowering, the ones in the vegetative state, even the clones isolated downstairs, in the extra room. When she finished that, Linda drove to the bank and withdrew $400 from his checking account. She then returned to the house, dropped his wallet into the mail slot, hit I-5 south, and flicked on the cruise control. She took her time this go-round, yet didn't dawdle: What had taken her thirteen hours nearly two years ago now took her twenty-four.

At ten that night came a banging on his front door and Manuel leapt out of his recliner, scrambled down the hall, grabbed the

.30-06 from the closet, and shimmied, his back to the wall, into his living room. He'd passed out early, his heart was still racing from a horrifying dream: Something, some invisible power, chasing him through a shopping mall, and whatever it was had just cornered him in the women's bathroom at Macy's. Manny shouldered the door open thinking only of his dream, the stupid mistake he'd made in it, and how he wouldn't be making it now. He almost shot the woman in the face when he realized who it was.

Linda walked into his house like she owned it. But it was Deborah who waved Manny's gun aside, shutting the door quickly behind her.

A Friend in Arcady

Walter Evans

"Turn here," she said. "Right here it is. Turn north here—Uh Rich—Uh Rober—" She paused a moment until her tongue and mind stumbled together. "Uh—Riley, right here."

"I can't turn north here, Grandma. We're going south right now."

"Oh," she said. "Well, turn here then."

"Ju-das priest!" Granddad slapped the seat top at Riley's back. "You ain't getting to no damn cemetery on that road. You're gonna go way on up here to a white church and turn on that road. Turn right. West."

"Can't turn here anyway, Grandma," Riley said. "They're grading the road up there."

"Goddamn dummies!" Granddad said, settling back. "Come out here and tear up a man's roads. What the hell good is making blacktop roads out of gravel roads if they're going to keep a man from getting anywhere on them? I'd like for some of them smartasses to tell me that." He cocked his head and jerked it toward each in turn, his stare fierce until it came to rest on the baby beside him.

Then, behind Riley, the baby began to whimper. Carla thumped her regularly on the back. "Well," she said, and then sighed loudly. "So, we're going to the cemetery, are we? I thought we were going to take Grandma to town to buy her a fresh Pepsi and then go on back home, Riley. What about that?"

"It's just right up here," Grandma said. "It won't be any trouble. We'll just turn north right up here."

"They told me to come down here," Riley said. "I don't know the way back. Can you find us a way back on your phone?"

"No coverage anywhere around here."

"Great."

"It's all right," she whispered loudly into the baby's ear. "It's all right, Baby Sue. Mommy will get you home as soon as she can."

"She's not wet, is she?" Riley asked, not looking back.

"Not yet," Carla said crisply.

"She's a good baby," Granddad said, his rough fingers plucking her pink blanket.

"Her's a good baby. Her don't cry unless something's a-hurting her."

"What about you, Grandma?" Riley glanced beside him at the thin paper pad resting beneath her thin cotton dress. "Grandma, you're all right, aren't you?"

"It's not very hot yet." A smug smile wrinkled her face. "Unless it's hot I don't generally sweat very much. Why don't you just turn north here—Uh Rya—Uh Riley?"

Riley drove absently, trying to to hurry, glancing often from the winding road to the uneven fields, sometimes newly culti-vated, the bare reddish dirt broken into evenly spaced rows of clods, some fields fluttering with broad-leaved corn sprouts or bushy soybeans or milo, some with scattered white-faced cattle browsing on rough hillsides among small oaks and large oaks, hedge trees along the fence line, a few willows bordering a pond, and everywhere small scattered stands of oak.

"Now look at that," Granddad said.

"It's pretty," Carla said brightly, after gazing for a moment into the stunted timber filling the unfenced fields on either side of the road ahead. "They're not big like redwood or gaudy like maple trees, but they are kind of pretty in a hard kind of way. Look into the shadows," she said, bringing the baby's head to the window. "Look into the shadows, and maybe you'll see a deer or something wild and nice, like when the Indians were here."

"Hell, they ought to kill that sonofabitch," Granddad said quietly. "A man letting the brush take his field like that. I seen this cleared off twice already, smooth as a woman's face, a young woman's. Hell, you could of planted anything in there or run a dozen head of strong cattle, and look at it now. Hell, it ain't worth a good goddamn any more."

He paused, lighting a cigarette as they passed the neighboring farm, the flame burning low on his large wooden match.

"That's the Jefferson place, or used to be—when me and Lewis Logan cleared it one summer. They ought to take him out and kill him now, the man that let it go like that. Hell, they ought to let *me* kill the worthless shit-licking, piss-guzzling sonofabitch!"

Carla sucked in a breath, her eyes blinking rapidly. "Will the deer come back?" she asked. "I mean if they let the trees grow back like that?"

Granddad threw out the blackened match and kept his face turned to the other window. "And *what* in the *hell* would a man want with brush and a goddamn deer when he ought to have cattle running on the goddamn place. Unless he was some sonofabitching loan company too busy stealing pennies off dead people's eyes to give a goddamn, or some worthless pall-bearing, coffin-robbing millionaire from Illinois who got too goddamn over-educated to know the value of a goddamn cow. Je-sus God all-*mighty!*"

"Well, there's sure a lot more meat on a cow than there is on a deer," Riley said.

They passed several fields in silence and dipped down to cross a stream trickling through a hard, dry bed. Riley's grandmother spoke as the car climbed a hill, swinging with the road to the right. "Your Great-granddaddy Tyler lived over there." She nodded toward a small one-story wooden house resting at the edge of the timber.

"And now they've let the goddamn brush take it," Granddad said. "Marie's daddy was as good a man as ever there was, and there never was a better. And now they let the brush take his farm."

"Did you ever live there, Grandma?" Riley asked.

"Yes." Her lips wrinkled into a smug smile and she nodded unsteadily several times.

"Hell, yes, she lived there," Granddad said. "Her and Carl and Louise and the whole first bunch of them kids. A goddamn fine living place once, too."

"Have we passed the cemetery?" Riley asked.

"Hell, no. You ain't even got to Columbia church."

Riley breathed deeply, then began to flush as his heart beat faster. He sensed an odor. "Carla," he asked quietly, "did the baby dirty her diaper?"

"No," Carla said. "I just looked."

"Do you feel all right, Grandma?"

"This is very nice, Riley," she said distinctly. "Thank you so much for taking me for a drive."

"I mean, do *you* feel all right, Grandma?"

She looked troubled and silently turned to the window. Riley felt hollow and sick.

"He wants to know did you ruin your pants, Marie," Granddad said quietly. "Which I don't believe you have."

Everyone was silent for almost a mile, when they came to a large white clapboard building decaying beside the road, the wood-shingled roof topped with an open steeple, which, Riley guessed, had once held a bell.

"Turn here," his grandfather said. As the car turned past the church Riley noticed large uneven letters graying against the narrow siding: Columbia Community Church.

"Great-granddad Rubinson lived on the far side," his grandfather said, barely glancing over. "Uncle Mason Tyler lived on the near side here, and Aunt Annie, she was an old maid, lived here all by herself."

Although Riley slowed, the fierce red-orange sun setting ahead moved into his vision, and he could only glance at the last toward a small unsteady cottage with a broken graying porch, dull siding of yellowish composition shingles, and a large black scar near a side window where shingles had torn away. Behind

239

the house two small ragged buildings stood in a bare lot, weeds growing high in front of the house and on either side.

"Don't know nobody in any of these goddamned houses any more," Granddad said.

"All dead and buried long ago. Don't know none of them now, and I used to know every man in the country, and the women too—and not just their names. I used to *know* them, everybody."

As Riley turned to nod in measured sympathy he noticed his grandmother tilting toward him, and abruptly wondered whether he should ask her if she could right herself or whether he should ask Carla, who had the baby, to do it. Riley would have straightened her himself, but he was driving, and besides he always washed his hands after touching his grandmother, and here he would be unable to wash. He noticed her withered hand clutching at the armrest and did nothing.

"If you want to, after this one we'll go to the oldest cemetery in the country," Granddad said. "Down by Arcady, where all the first settlers lived around here, where your grandma and I were young. But, of course, we won't go if you don't want to."

"Sure," Riley said, "that's fine."

"It's all right, Susie," Carla whispered loudly. "Mommy loves you. Mommy will take care of you."

Ahead, in the setting sun's violet reddish glare, the rocky dirt road fell steeply down, and on either side scrubby weeds edged high banks of sandy rocky soil.

"Go slow," Granddad said quietly. "You'll turn in to the left here when you come to the gate."

Farther down the bank lowered to road level, and a rough dirt driveway led over the roadside ditch into a pasture. Riley felt doubtful as he gently nosed his car off the road and stopped at the wire gate. Ahead he saw only a sparse hilly pasture with scattered trees and a few lazing cattle. Then, several yards up on the hillside, on the crest, he saw a wire fence surrounding a cluster of high, thin stones.

"Well, we got where we're going," Granddad said. "The gate won't be locked."

Riley got out, loosed the light chain, swung the gate open, and drove through. His grandfather had to remind him to shut the gate behind them. He parked the car beneath a grove of trees where several cattle lay casting long shadows in the dying sunlight.

"You go on without me," Grandma said. "You all get out and walk through the graveyard."

Riley got out, and his grandfather followed silently. Carla handed the baby to Riley. "Should we open Grandma's door?" she asked. "It might be cooler for her."

"No," Riley said. "She might fall out."

Granddad had passed ahead through the gate, gently closing it behind him, and began ranging slowly from one headstone to the next. Just inside the gate Riley held the softly crying baby and stood next to Carla, watching his grandfather's progress.

"Why do people have to get so old and ugly and helpless," she said, and began to move forward, expecting no answer.

"Because," Riley said, "now I've thought about this—because they're going to have to die. And because when they get old enough they're going to be ready to die, and other people are going to be ready for them to. It's probably better this way. More—Well, makes death kind of friend-like in a way."

"Death," she said. "A friend?"

"Kind of like a friend, in a way."

Without responding, Carla roughly took the child and began to stride through the cemetery. The grass grew dry and sparse in some places, a few clumps and brownish streaks showing it had been recently mowed. Carla walked past three or four new marble headstones and a row of graves marked only by metal tags to an old unevenly rounded slab of thin white stone. Riley stepped behind her, saw lettering too smooth to be read. Near the top a roughly carved pair of clasped hands mutely pointed above. As they passed on through the cemetery they stopped at several other old stones, some broken, barely legible, only a few with names—Smith, Tyree, Foster, Hickman—some with dates as far back as the 1840's, a few rough headstones rudely carved from thin slabs of native rock impossible to read. Finally, Carla took the sleeping baby and, telling Riley it was time to go, strode back to the car.

Riley walked over to his grandfather, standing quietly beneath a blighted cedar, the cemetery's only tree. "Where is our family?" he asked. His grandfather clumsily gestured toward a group of stones near the corner. Riley went over to read a few names—Taylor, Rubinson, Callahan—and a few dates and then moved back. "Well," he asked, "are you ready to go now?"

His grandfather glanced up at him sharply, then looked back to the stone at his foot. "I knew them all," he said. "Every damn one of them, or their families, in this whole goddamn boneyard. Now ain't that hell." He slowly moved to the next stone. "This one," he said, "DePreux ain't it?" Riley nodded. The stone was only twenty years old, and not hard to read.

Him and me ran in a bunch when we was kids, the wildest goddamn bunch this town ever did see. And now he's dead and every damn one of them. Now ain't that hell when you get to thinking about it." Riley nodded stiffly.

"But it's kept nice," Granddad said, "for a boneyard. And a lot of them ain't. No groundhogs and snakes, and I suppose that's something." He was near the end of the last row, and when he reached the end he turned and began walking straight toward the gate only to stop a few feet away.

"That's Susan Freeman." He nodded toward a low stone. "Susan, like the baby."

Riley stopped to read it. "Ford," he said, "Susan Ford."

"Ford don't count. That's her married name. Wasn't married six months and she was dead. Her sister died the same time, Berthy Freeman, the finest woman there ever was in this country, over in Arcady. No man ever loved any like I loved her. If there was still a town there Berthy'd still be the most beautiful woman ever been in it. Died eighteen years old, a year or so before your grandma and me got married, when your grandma was young and pretty like she used to be, and not ugly and old and dirtying herself and her mind gone to hell and hell to be around. And there's Berthy over in Arcady now. Died at eighteen, and young and pretty when she died, and not a goddamn man ever knew what for. I would always dream—"

He stood for several seconds, unmoving. Riley hoped his grandfather would not cry, for he had been told that the old man cried easily now.

"I been good to Marie anyhow," the old man said. "Where's Marie now? I want her. I want to see her."

Riley was startled. "In the car." He led toward the gate. "Over here."

"She's in the car, ain't she?" the old man said. "I know she's in the car."

Riley closed the gate behind them. His grandfather hurried ahead and had kissed his wife and had already begun telling her in a nervous voice how well the cemetery was kept when Riley got in the car.

"It's dry," he was saying. "There ain't no moisture seeping in there anywhere. And they keep it clean, and the grass is good. They'll keep it up good."

When they had driven out of the pasture and Riley closed the final gate behind them, Carla asked him if he was finally ready to to back, now that it was nearly dark, and long after the child's suppertime.

"No," the old man said. "We're going to Arcady Cemetery. It ain't very far from here."

"Let's go," his grandmother said. "Arcady's such a nice town. Your granddad knows someone there. I want to go there now."

"Well," Riley said, "I don't know. Carla, what do you think?"

"Go!" she said. "Go, go, go!"

"You see," his grandmother said smugly. "I told you so. We'll go on to Arcady. I think I want to live there."

"Where is it?" Riley asked.

"Je-sus *Christ!*" the old man broke out suddenly. "You don't you know a goddamn thing, do you? Dumber than a piss-drunk spotted assed ape!"

"Turn north here," his grandmother said. "It's up north here."

"Hell, no," the old man said. "It's west. My grandpa used to take this road here in a horse and wagon, take it straight to Arcady."

Riley edged out of the drive and began to nose his car down the steep dirt road, toward the dying sun's fierce glare. "What in the hell do you think you're doing now?" the old man shouted. "If you're not the dumbest, most ignoramous-est, chuckle-headed, knuckleheaded ten ton dummy I've never seen nor heard of!"

"Arcady?"

"Jes-us *Christ!* You'll kill us all down this road! There's a bluff at the bottom of that road the likes of which you've never seen in your goddamned life, and the whole goddamn thing dead ends in a goddamn cave!"

"You said the road—"

"*The hell I did!* I said it *used* to! Now turn this goddamn sonofabitch around and I'll tell you when to turn. Jesus God almighty, I never seen anything like it in my life."

Nervously, Riley drove back to the main road and on through the outskirts of Ashendon, where his grandparents had lived just after they were married, and where they had raised Riley's father. Riley and his grandmother wanted to stop by the house before darkness came, but the old man forced them on to Arcady, urging the car faster and faster until it madly threw gravel and dirt behind them, passing houses and fields at which Granddad would shout, "Old Vespucci's place, as good an Italian as ever was in the country, and now he's dead," and "The Mather boys' place, and that old house was as fine a house as there is in the country, and some son of a bitch bought it and abandoned it, and when I find him I'm gonna kill the dou-ble-damned horseshit swilling sonofabitch!"

"We passed the road, Dad," Grandma said.

"The hell we did, Mommy! It ain't passed till we pass Buddy Graham's and goddamn if it's been passed. He'll be out front on a bench behind the biggest table of food ever seen in the country. He was every day of his life, and goddamn if he ain't there yet."

They drove on until it was certain they had gone too far, and as they returned the old man made Riley drive slowly, cursing him for his haste. Riley turned on the car lights and drove fast as he dared.

"Goddamn, they've changed the whole goddamn country. It don't look nothing like it did. I drove the road to Arcady a thousand times and never seen the day yet it couldn't be found. Graham's is there! Bygod, there it is, and there ain't no road."

Riley slowed as the old man quieted. An abandoned farmhouse sat back from the road, trees poking out through broken roof, a part of one side burned away.

"Some worthless sonofabitch bought out Graham and ruined it in a month. It's happened in a month," the old man said. "I know because not a month ago today I sat in this yard and ate watermelon with Buddy Graham and his widow."

"There's a track across the road," Carla said uneasily. "But, Riley, we can't drive in there."

"There it is!" the old man cried, and suddenly Riley found himself fighting to twist away from the bony fingers pinching into his shoulder. "I knew it was here all the time," he yelled. "Now get in there!"

Riley had turned from the pressure in his shoulder until his face was inches from that of the old man and the old man's wild burning eyes. "Now you get in there!" he said fiercely.

Riley glanced, in the last of the sun's faint reddish light, at the overgrown two-rutted track leading into the dark timber. "I'm not going in there," Riley said, shaking his head. "Listen, I really hope you don't think I'm going in there."

"Let's go on," Grandma said thickly. "Let's go north."

The old man grabbed Riley's ear and the side of his face in a bony fist. "Get in there," he breathed hoarsely. "You sissy-pissing, woman-cocked coward! Bygod, I'll skin you alive, ram my fist down your throat, snatch your asshole, and jerk you inside out! Goddamn you, get in there!"

Slowly, the car bounced ahead, jerking from rut to rut, headlights drawing strange weaving shadows from the dark trees and wild undergrowth. Then, as Riley hesitantly braked, the old man crushed him against the steering wheel, shoving back as he leapt from the car.

"Goddamn," he breathed hoarsely, stepping into the dark timber. "They let the brush take it! Mommy, where is it? The brush took Arcady."

Riley glanced over at his grandmother. In the dim light he could see her head resting at a crazy angle between the car door and the dashboard. She breathed heavily, pale lids loosely muffling her eyes, the tip of her tongue visible at the corner of her unclosed mouth. Where one withered leg angled above the other he saw thick brown fluid fouling the pad under his grandmother, seeping across the seat. The stench was oppressive.

Carla whispered as the baby began to cry. "Riley? Riley, are you all right?"

"Sure," he said. "What about you and Sue?"

"I think she's all right. Riley, please get us out of here!"

"Granddad's in there," he said. "Let me get him."

"Let him go," she said. "Let him go or let him find us outside. But please, get us out of here."

Riley hesitated, then abruptly started the car and began to back away blindly, when suddenly from the darkness the old man stumbled on them, waving his arms, bouncing in and out of the blinding headlights, tears wet in his wild eyes.

"My God, Berthy, Berthy," he cried in a hoarse whisper. "The stones is all down, and the graves is all scattered and the groundhogs and snakes has got into the graves! Jesus Christ. O goddamn! Jesus Christ."

Greasy Lake

T. Coraghessan Boyle

There was a time when courtesy and winning ways went out of style, when it was good to be bad, when you cultivated decadence like a taste. We were all dangerous characters then. We wore torn-up leather jackets, slouched around with toothpicks in our mouths, sniffed glue and ether and what somebody claimed was cocaine. When we wheeled our parents' whining station wagons out into the street we left a patch of rubber half a block long. We drank gin and grape juice, Tango, Thunderbird, and Bali Hai. We were nineteen. We were bad. We read André Gide and struck elaborate poses to show we didn't give a shit about anything. At night, we went up to Greasy Lake.

Through the center of town, up the strip, past the housing developments and shopping malls, street lights giving way to the thin streaming illumination of the headlights, trees crowding the asphalt in a black unbroken wall: that was the way out to Greasy Lake. The Indians had called it Wakan, a reference to the clarity of its waters. Now it was fetid and murky, the mud banks glittering with broken glass and strewn with beer cans and the charred remains of bonfires. There was a single ravaged island a hundred yards from shore, so stripped of vegetation it looked as if the air force had strafed it. We went up to the lake because everyone went there, because we wanted to sniff the rich scent of possibility on the breeze, watch a girl take off her clothes and plunge into the festering murk, drink beer, smoke pot, howl at the stars, savor the incongruous full-throated roar of rock and roll against the primeval susurrus of frogs and crickets. This was nature.

I was there one night, late, in the company of two dangerous characters. Digby wore a gold star in his right ear and allowed his father to pay his tuition at Cornell; Jeff was thinking of quitting school to become a painter/musician/headshop proprietor. They were both expert in the social graces, quick with a sneer, able to manage a Ford with lousy shocks over rutted and gutted blacktop road at eighty-five while rolling a joint as compact as a Tootsie Roll Pop stick. They could lounge against a bank of booming speakers and trade "man's" with the best of them or roll out across the dance floor as if their joints worked on bearings. They were slick and quick and they wore their mirror shades at breakfast and dinner, in the shower, in closets and caves. In short, they were bad.

I drove. Digby pounded on the dashboard and shouted along with Toots & the Maytals while Jeff hung his head out the window and streaked the side of my mother's Bel Air with vomit. It was early June, the air soft as a hand on your cheek, the third night of summer vacation. The first two nights we'd been out till dawn, looking for something we never found. On this, the third night, we'd cruised the strop sixty-seven times, been in and out of every bar and club we could think of in a twenty-mile radius, stopped twice for bucket chicken and forty-cent hamburgers, debated going to a party at the house of a girl Jeff's sister knew, and chucked two dozen raw eggs and mailboxes and hitchhikers. It was 2:00 A.M.; the bars were closing. There was nothing to do but take a bottle of lemon-flavored gin up to Greasy Lake.

The taillights of a single car winked at us as we swung into the dirt lot with its tufts of weed and washboard corrugations; '57 Chevy, mint, metallic blue. On the far side of the lot, the exoskeleton of some gaunt chrome insect, a chopper leaned against its kickstand. And that was it for excitement: some junkie half-wit biker and a car freak pumping his girlfriend. Whatever it was we were looking for, we weren't about to find it at Greasy Lake. Not that night.

But then all of a sudden Digby was fighting for the wheel. "Hey, that's Tony Lovett's car! Hey!" he shouted, while I stabbed at the brake pedal and the Bel Air nosed up to the gleaming bumper of the parked Chevy. Digby leaned on the horn, laughing, and instructed me to put my brights on. I flicked on the brights. This was hilarious. A joke. Tony would experience premature withdrawal and expect to be confronted by grim-looking state troopers with flashlights. We hit the horn, strobed the lights, and then jumped out of the car to press out witty faces to Tony's windows; for all we knew we might even catch a glimpse of some little fox's tit, and then we could slap backs with the red-faced Tony, roughhouse a little, and go on to new heights of adventure and daring.

The first mistake, the one that opened the whole floodgate, was losing my grip on the keys. In the excitement, leaping from the car with the gin in one hand and a roach clip in the other, I spilled them in the grass—in the dark, rank, mysterious night-time grass of Greasy Lake. This was a tactical error, as damaging and irreversible in its was as Westmoreland's decision to dig in at Khe Sanh. I felt it like a jab of intuition, and I stopped there by the open door, peering vaguely into the night that puddled up round my feet.

The second mistake—and this was inextricably bound up with the first was identifying the car as Tony Lovett's. Even before the very bad character in greasy jeans and engineer boots ripped out of the driver's door, I began to realize that this chrome blue was much lighter than the robin's-egg of Tony's car, and that Tony's car didn't have rear-mounted speakers. Judging from their expressions, Digby and Jeff were privately groping toward the same inevitable and unsettling conclusion as I was.

In any case, there was no reasoning with this bad greasy character—clearly he was a man of action. The first lusty Rockette kick of his steel-toed boot caught me under the chin, chipped my favorite tooth, and left me sprawled in the dirt. Like a fool, I'd gone down on one knee to comb the stiff hacked grass for the keys, my mind making connections in the most dragged out, testudineous way, knowing that things had gone wrong, that I was in a lot of trouble, and that the lost ignition key was my grail and my salvation. The three or four succeeding blows were mainly absorbed by my right buttock and the tough piece of bone at the base of my spine.

Meanwhile, Digby vaulted the kissing bumpers and delivered a savage kung-fu blow to the greasy character's collarbone. Digby had just finished a course in martial arts for phys-ed credit and had spent the better part of the past two nights telling us apocryphal tales of Bruce Lee types and of the raw power invested in lightning blows shot from coiled wrists, ankles, and elbows. The greasy character was unimpressed. He merely backed off a step, his face like a Toltec mask, and laid Digby out with a single whistling roundhouse blow … but by now Jeff had got into the act, and I was beginning to extricate myself from the dirt, a tinny compound of shock, rage, and impotence wadded in my throat.

Jeff was on the guy's back, biting at his ear. Digby was on the ground, cursing, I went for the tire iron I kept under the driver's seat. I kept it there because bad characters always keep tire irons under the driver's seat, for just such an occasion as this. Never mind that I hadn't been involved in a fight since sixth grade, when a kid with a sleepy eye and two streams of mucus depending from his nostrils hit me in the knee with a Louisville slugger, never mind that I'd touched the tire iron exactly twice before, to change tires: it was there. And I went for it.

I was terrified. Blood was beating in my ears, my hands were shaking, my heart turning over like a dirt bike in the wrong gear. My antagonist was shirtless, and a single cord of muscle flashed across his chest as he bent forward to peel Jeff from his back like a wet overcoat. "Motherfucker," he spat, over and over, and I was aware in that all four of us—Digby, Jeff, and myself included—were chanting "motherfucker, motherfucker," as if it were a battle cry. (What happened next? The detective asks the murderer from beneath the turned-down brim of his porkpie hat. I don't know, the murderer says, something came over me. Exactly.)

Digby poled the flat of his hand in the bad character's face and I came at him like a kamikaze, mindless, raging, stung with humiliation—the whole thing, from the initial boot to the chin to this murderous primal instant involving no more than sixty hyperventilating, gland-flooding seconds—I came at him and brought the tire iron down across his ear. The effect was instantaneous, astonishing. He was a stunt man and this was Hollywood, he was a big grimacing toothy balloon and I was a man with a straight pin. He collapsed. Wet his pants. Went loose in his boots.

A single second, big as a zeppelin, floated by. We were standing over him in a circle, gritting our teeth, jerking our necks, our limbs and hands and feet twitching with glandular discharges. No one said anything. We just started down at the guy, the car freak, the lover, the bad greasy character laid low. Digby looked at me; so did Jeff. I was still holding the tire iron, a tuft of hair clinging to the crook like dandelion fluff, like down. Rattled, I dropped it in the dirt, already envisioning the headline, the pitted faces of the police inquisitors, the gleam of handcuffs, clank of bars, the big black shadows rising from the back of the cell ... when suddenly a raw torn shriek cut through me like all the juice in all the electric chairs in the country.

It was the fox. She was short, barefoot, dressed in panties and a man's shirt. "Animals!" she screamed, running at us with her fists clenched and wisps of blow-dried hair in her face. There was a silver chain around her ankle, and her toenails flashed in the glare of the headlights, I think it was the toenails that did it. Sure, the gin and the cannabis and even the Kentucky Fried may have had a hand in it, but it was the sight of those flaming toes that set us off—the toad emerging from the loaf in hidden *Virgin Spring*, lipstick smeared on a child: she was already tainted. We were on her like Bergman's deranged brothers—see no evil, hear none, speak none—panting, wheezing, tearing at her clothes, grabbing for flesh. We were bad characters, and we were scared and hot and three steps over the line—anything could have happened.

251

It didn't.

Before we could pin her to the hood of the car, our eyes masked with lust and greed and the purest primal badness, a pair of headlights swung into the lot. There we were, dirty, bloody, guilty, dissociated from humanity and civilization, the first of the Ur-crimes behind us, second in progress, shreds of nylon panty and spandex brassiere dangling from our fingers, our flies open, lips licked—there we were, caught in the spotlight. Nailed.

We bolted. First for the car, and then, realizing we had no way of starting it, for the woods. I thought nothing. I thought escape. The headlights came at me like accusing fingers. I was gone.

Ram-bam-bam, across the parking lot, past the chopper and into the feculent undergrowth at the lake's edge, insects flying up in my face, weeds whipping, frogs and snakes and red-eyed turtles splashing off into the night: I was already ankle-deep in muck and tepid water and still going strong. Behind me, the girl's scream rose in intensity, disconsolate, incriminating, the screams of the Sabine women, the Christian martyrs, Anne Frank dragged from the garret. I kept going, pursued by those cries, imagining cops and bloodhounds. The water was up to my knees when I realized what I was doing: I was going to swim for it. Swim the breadth of Greasy Lake and hide myself in the thick clot of woods on the far side. They'd never find me there!

I was breathing in sobs, in gasps. The water lapped at my waist as I looked out over the moon-burnished ripples, the mats of algae that clung to the surface like scabs. Digby and Jeff had vanished. I paused. Listened. The girl was quieter now, screams tapering to sobs, but there were male voices, angry, excited, and the high-pitched ticking of the second car's engine. I waded deeper, stealthy, hunted, the ooze sucking at my sneakers. As I was about to take the plunge—at the very instant I dropped my shoulder for the first slashing stroke—I blundered into something. Something unspeakable, obscene, something soft, wet, moss-grown. A patch of weed? A log? When I reached out to touch it, it gave like a rubber duck, it gave like flesh.

In one of those nasty little epiphanies for which we are prepared by films and TV and childhood visits to the funeral home to ponder the shrunken painted forms of dead grandparents, I understood what it was that bobbed there so inadmissibly in the dark. Understood, and stumbled back in horror and revulsion, my mind yanked in six different directions (I was nineteen, a mere child, an infant, and here in the space of five minutes I'd struck down one greasy character and blundered into the water-logged carcass of a second), thinking, the keys, the keys, why did I have to go and lose the keys? I stumbled back, but the muck took hold of my feet—a sneaker snagged, balance lost—and suddenly I was pitching face forward into the buoyant black mass, throwing out my hands in desperation while simultaneously conjuring the image of reeking frogs and muskrats and revolving in slicks of their own deliquescing juices. AAAAArrrgh! I shot from the water like a torpedo, the dead man rotating to expose a mossy beard and eyes cold as the moon. I must have shouted out, thrashing around in the weeds, because the voices behind me suddenly became animated.

"What was that?"

"It's them, it's them: they tried to, tried to … *rape* me!" Sobs.

A man's voice, flat Midwestern accent. "You sons a bitches, we'll kill you!"

Frogs, crickets.

Then another voice, harsh, *r*-less, Lower East Side: "Motherfucker!" I recognized the verbal virtuosity of the bad greasy character in the engineer boots. Tooth chipped, sneakers gone, coated in mud and slime and worse, crouching breathless in the weeds waiting to have my ass thoroughly and definitively kicked and fresh from the hideous stinking embrace of a three-days-dead-corpse, I suddenly felt the rush of joy and vindication: the son of a bitch was alive! Just as quickly, my bowels tuned to ice. "Come on out of there, you pansy mothers!" the bad greasy character was screaming. He shouted curses until he was out of breath.

The crickets started up again, then the frogs. All at once there was a sound in the reeds, a swishing, a splash: thunk-a-thunk. They were throwing rocks. The frogs fell silent. I cradled my head. Swish; swish, thunk-a-thunk. A wedge of feldspar the size of a cue ball glanced off my knee. I bit my finger.

It was then that they turned to the car. I heard a door slam, a curse, and then the sound of headlights shattering—almost a good-natured sound, celebratory, like corks popping from the necks of bottles. This was succeeded by the dull booming of the fenders, metal on metal, and then the icy crash of the windshield. I inched forward, elbows and knees, my belly pressed to the muck, thinking of guerillas and commandos and *The Naked and the Dead*. I parted the weeds and squinted the length of the parking lot.

The second car—it was a Trans-Am—was still running, its high beams washing the scene in a lurid stagy light. Tire iron flailing, the greasy bad character was laying into the side of my mother's Bel Air like an avenging demon, his shadow riding up the trunks of the trees. Whomp. Whomp. Whomp-whomp. The other two guys—blond types, in fraternity jackets—were helping out with tree branches and skull-sized boulders. One of them was gathering up bottles, rocks, muck, candy wrappers, used condoms, pop-tops, and other refuse and pitching it through the window on the driver's side. I could see the fox, a white bulb behind the windshield of the '57 Chevy. "Bobbie," she whined over the thumping, "come *on*." The greasy character paused a moment, took one good swipe at the left tail light, then heaved the tire iron halfway across the lake. Then he fired up the '57 and was gone.

Blond head nodded at blond head. One said something to the other, too low for me to catch. They were no doubt thinking that in helping to annihilate my mother's car they'd committed a fairly rash act, and thinking too that there were three bad characters connected with that very car watching them from the woods. Perhaps other possibilities occurred to them as well—

police, jail cells, justices of the peace, reparations, lawyers, irate parents, fraternal censure. Whatever they were thinking, they suddenly dropped branches, bottles, and rocks and sprang for their car in unison, as if they'd choreographed it. Five seconds. That's all it took. The engine shrieked, the tires squealed, a cloud of dust rose from the rutted lot and then settled back on darkness.

I don't know how long I lay there, the bad breath of decay all around me, my jacket heavy as a bear, the primordial ooze subtly reconstituting itself to accommodate my upper thighs and testicles. My jaws ached, my knee throbbed, my coccyx was on fire. I contemplated suicide, wondered if I'd need bridge-work, scraped the recesses of my brain for some sort of excuse to give my parents—a tree had fallen on the car, I was blindsided by a bread truck, hit and run, vandals got to it while I was playing chess at Digby's. Then I thought of the dead man. He was probably the only person on the planet worse off than I was. I thought about him, fog on the lake, insects chirring eerily, and felt the tug of fear, felt the darkness opening up inside me like a set of jaws. Who was he, I wondered, the victim of time and circumstance bobbing sorrowfully in the lake at my back. The owner of the chopper, no doubt, a bad older character come to this. Shot during a murky drug deal, drowned while drunkenly frolicking in the lake. Another headline. My car was wrecked; he was dead.

When the eastern half of the sky went from black to cobalt and the trees began to separate themselves from the shadows, I pushed myself up from the mud and stepped out into the open. By now the birds had begun to take over for the crickets, and dew lay slick on the leaves. There was a smell in the air, raw and sweet at the same time, the smell of the sun firing buds and opening blossoms. I contemplated the car. It lay there like a wreck along the highway, like a steel sculpture left over from a vanished civilization. Everything was still. This was nature.

I was circling the car, as dazed and bedraggled as the sole

survivor of an air blitz, when Digby and Jeff emerged from the trees behind me. Digby's face was cross-hatched with smears of dirt; Jeff's jacket was gone and his shirt was torn across the shoulder. They slouched across the lot, looking sheepish, and silently came up beside me to gape at the ravaged automobile. No one said a word. After a while, Jeff swung open the driver's side door and began to scoop the broken glass and garbage off the seat. I looked at Digby. He shrugged. "At least they didn't slash the tires," he said.

It was true, the tires were intact. There was no windshield, the headlights were staved in, and the body looked if it had been sledgehammered for a quarter a shot at the county fair, but the tires were inflated to regulation pressure. The car was drivable. In silence, all three of us bent to scrape the mud and shattered glass from the interior. I said nothing about the biker. When we were finished, I cursed myself, and turned to search the grass. I spotted them almost immediately, no more than five feet from the open door, glinting like jewels in the first tapering shaft of sunlight. There was no reason to get philosophical about it: I eased into the seat and turned the engine over.

It was at that precise moment that the silver Mustang with the flame decals rumbled into the lot. All three of us froze; then Digby and Jeff slid into the car and slammed the door. We watched as the Mustang rocked and bobbed across the ruts and finally jerked to a halt beside the forlorn chopper at the far end of the lot. "Let's go," Digby said. I hesitated, the Bel Air wheezing beneath me.

Two girls emerged from the Mustang. Tight jeans, stiletto heels, hair like frozen fur. They bent over the motorcycle, paced back and forth aimlessly, glanced once or twice at us, then ambled over to where the reeds sprang up in a green fence round the perimeter of the lake. One of them cupped her hands to her to her mouth. "Al," she called, "Hey, Al!"

"Come on," Digby hissed. "Let's get out of here."

But it was too late. The second girl was picking her way across the lot, unsteady on her heels, looking up at us and then away. She was older—twenty-five or -six—and as she came closer we could see there was something wrong with her: she was stoned or drunk, lurching now and waving her arms for balance. I gripped the steering wheel as if it were the ejection lever of a flaming jet, and Digby spat out my name, twice, terse and impatient

"Hi." The girl said.

We looked at her like zombies, like war veterans, like deaf-and-dumb pencil peddlers.

She smiled, her lips cracked and dry. "Listen," she said, bending from the waist to look in the window, "you guys seen Al?" Her pupils were pinpoints, her eyes glass. She jerked her neck. "That's his bike over there—Al's. You seen him?"

Al. I didn't know what to say. I wanted to get out of the car and retch. I wanted to go home to my parents' house and crawl into bed. Digby poked me in the ribs. "We haven't seen anybody," I said.

The girl seemed to consider this, reaching out a slim veiny arm to brace herself against the car. "No matter," she said, slurring the *t*'s, "he'll turn up." And then, as if she'd just taken stock of the whole scene—the ravaged car and our battered faces, the desolation of the place—she said: "Hey, you guys look like some pretty bad characters—been fightin', huh?" We stared straight ahead, rigid as catatonics. She was fumbling in her pocket and muttering something. Finally, she held out a handful of tablets in glassine wrappers. "Hey, you want to party, you want to do some of these with me and Sarah?"

I just looked at her. I thought I was going to cry. Digby broke the silence. "No, thanks," he said, leaning over me. "Some other time."

I put the car in gear and it inched forward with a groan, shaking off pellets of glass like an old dog shedding water after a bath, heaving over the ruts on its worn springs, creeping toward the highway. There was a sheen of sun on the lake. I looked back. The girl was still standing there, watching us, her shoulders slumped, hand outstretched.

Acknowledgments

"Greasy Lake," copyright © 1982 by T. Corraghessan Boyle; from *Greasy Lake and Other Stories* by T. Coraghessan Boyle. Used by permission of Viking Books, an imprint of Penguin Publishing Group, a division of Penguin Random House LLC. All rights reserved.

Elizabeth Bruce's "The Grass Jesus Walked On" was previously published in the online journal *Literally Stories*, in the edition published 5 December 2018

Ulrick Casmir's "Phantom Power" previously appeared in Casmir's debut story collection, *Children of the Night: Stories.*

Michael' Darcher's "Jackpots Only" originally appeared in The Carolina Quarterly, Vol.49 no. 2, Winter 1997.

Michael Gaspeny's "Once I Lived Like a Stoop-Shouldered Idol" originally appeared in *moonShine* review, Fall/Winter 2021 (Volume 17, Issue 2).

Jen Knox's "The Lavender House" appears in her forthcoming novel *We Arrive Uninvited*

Misty Skaggs' "Where to Buy Your Weed" originally appeared on friedchickenandcoffee.com on December 15, 2012.

Luis Alberto Urrea's "Barrio Walden" originally appeared in the May/June 2013 issue of *Orion Magazine.*

Contributors

Dorothy Allison is the author of *Bastard Out Of Carolina, Trash,* and *The Women Who Hate Me*, as well as *Skin: Talking About Sex, Class and Literature.*

Hillary Behrman's stories have appeared or are forthcoming in *The Madison Review, High Desert Journal* and *New Ohio Review.* She is the recipient of the 2020 Chris O'Malley Prize in Fiction and her work has been recognized in *Glimmer Train.* Hillary is a graduate of Pacific University's MFA in Writing Program, and she lives in Seattle, Washington.

Henri Bensussen has published stories and poems in various journals, including *So To Speak, Common Ground Review, Behind the Yellow Wallpaper: New Tales of Madness*, and in Lisa Locasio's *Golden State 2017: Best New Writing from California.* A chapbook of poems, *Earning Colors* was published by Finishing Line Press, 2015. She has a B.A. in Biology and once lived by the sea, but now she lives in Santa Rosa, California.

T. Coraghessan Boyle is the author of twenty-eight books of fiction, including, most recently, *The Relive Box* (2017) and *Outside Looking In* (2019). He received a Ph.D. degree in Nineteenth Century British Literature from the University of Iowa in 1977, and has been a member of the English Department at the University of Southern California since 1978, where he is Distinguished Professor of English. His work has been translated into more than two dozen languages. His stories have appeared in most of the major American magazines, including *The New Yorker, Harper's, Esquire*, and more. He has been the recipient of a number of literary awards, including the PEN/Faulkner Prize for best novel of the year (*World's End,* 1988); the PEN/Malamud Prize in the short story (*T.C. Boyle Stories,*

1999); and the Prix Médicis Étranger for best foreign novel in France (*The Tortilla Curtain,* 1997). He currently lives near Santa Barbara with his wife and three children. His thirtieth book comes out this year, a collection titled *I Walk Between the Raindrops*, followed by a new novel, *Blue Skies*, next year.

DC-based Texas writer **Elizabeth Bruce's** debut novel, *And Silent Left the Place* (new edition released in 2021), won Washington Writers' Publishing House's Fiction Award and distinctions from *ForeWord Magazine* and the Texas Institute of Letters. She's published prose across the globe and received fellowships from the DC Commission on the Arts & Humanities and McCarthey Dressman Education Foundation. This story is part of her unpublished collection, *Universally Adored and Other One Dollar Stories,* in which each fiction begins with the words "one dollar" and pivots in some way around the "universally adored" dollar. Her website is: https://www.elizabethbrucedc.com

Ulrick Casimir Originally from the USVI, Ulrick Casimir holds an M.F.A. in Fiction from UNC-Greensboro and a Ph.D. in English from the University of Oregon, where he currently teaches. His short fiction has most often appeared in *Plainsongs. Children of the Night: Stories*, his debut collection, was published by Corpus Callosum Press in spring of 2018.

Michael Darcher, a product of the University of Montana's MFA Program, taught English for a quarter century at Pierce College, a community college in Washington state. His fiction has appeared in *High Plains Literary Review, Green Mountains Review, The Carolina Quarterly, The Nebraska Review, Rio Grande Review*, and elsewhere. One story was nominated for a Pushcart Prize. Michael resides above Commencement Bay in Tacoma with his wife, Joanne.

George Drew is the author of nine poetry collections, including

Pastoral Habits: New and Selected Poems and *The View from Jackass Hill*, winner of the 2010 X.J. Kennedy Poetry Prize, both from Texas Review Press, *Fancy's Orphan* (Tiger Bark Press) and most recently *Drumming Armageddon* (Madville). Drew also has published a chapbook, *So Many Bones: Poems of Russia*. He has a new chapbook coming out titled *Hog: A Delta Memoir* (Bass Clef Press), and a book of essays *Just Like Oz* (Madville).

Stephanie Dupal is a Franco-Canadian writer and associate professor who teaches writing and literature in Virginia. Her work most recently appeared in *Fiction International, Broad River Review*, and *Little Patuxent Review*, among others, and in magazines in the UK and Norway. She awaits the acceptance and publication of her short story collection, *The Kindness of Terrible People*, and her novel, *In This Age of Hard Trying*. Please visit: www.stephaniedupal.com.

Walter Evans is a graduate of the University of Missouri and the University of Chicago, and he has published a dozen stories in *Peregrine, Cimarron Review, Kansas Quarterly, Chelsea*, and elsewhere. He takes far more pride in his three sons than in anything else he has ever had a part in creating.

Michael Gaspeny is the author of the novella in verse, *The Tyranny of Questions* (Unicorn Press) and the chapbooks *Re-Write Men* and *Vocation*. He has won the Randall Jarrell Poetry Competition and the O. Henry Festival Short Fiction Contest. His novel, *Postcard from the Delta*, is forthcoming from Livingston Press. For hospice service, he has received The (North Carolina) Governor's Award for Volunteer Excellence.

Roger Hart's stories and essays have been published in *Natural Bridge, The Tampa Review, Passages North, Runner's World*, and other magazines and journals. His story "Mysteries of the Universe" won the McGlinn Fiction Prize and was published in Philadelphia

Stories. He recently moved to Montana where he's working on a novel under the supervision of his wife and two big dogs.

David Hartshorne is a writer, teacher, and potter in the Chicago area. He received his MFA in Creative Writing from Converse College (now Converse University) in Spartanburg, SC and in 2021 was a finalist for the inaugural Converse MFA Alumni Book Prize.

Suzanne Heagy is a writer, teacher, and editor. Her first novel, *Love Lets Us Down* (2015), was recognized in the 18th annual Foreword Reviews' INDIEFAB Book of the Year Awards. Her short stories have appeared in *The Anthology of Appalachian Literature, Schuylkill Valley Journal*, and *Pleiades*, among others. Suzanne is a member of the women's collective, The Gloria Sirens, and writes a monthly column for their blog at https://thegloriasirens.com.

Jen Knox is an award-winning author and speaker who teaches writing, meditation, and yoga. Her short fiction can be found in *The Best Small Fictions, Chicago Tribune, Chicago Quarterly Review, Room Magazine*, and *The Saturday Evening Post*. Her collections include *The Glass City* (Prize Americana winner), *Resolutions* (AUX Media), and *After the Gazebo* (Pen/Faulkner nominee). Her debut novel, *We Arrive Uninvited*, is the 2021 Prose Award winner from Steel Toe Books and will be available in Fall 2022.

Mark Lammers writes about the confluences of people, place and memory. He is currently working on a memoir about his experiences as a Peace Corps volunteer in West Africa in the late '80s. He can be reached at marklammerswrites.com.

Robert Garner McBrearty's stories have appeared in many places including the Pushcart Prize, *Missouri Review, Narrative, North American Review* and *Ellery Queen's Mystery Magazine*. He is the author of five books of fiction and the recipient of a Sherwood Anderson Foundation Fiction Grant. His stories have been performed on stage at the Texas Bound show at the Dallas Museum of Art and at Stories on Stage in Denver.

Jayne Anne Phillips is the author of five novels, *Quiet Dell, Lark and Termite, Motherkind, Shelter,* and *Machine Dreams,* and two widely anthologized story collections, *Fast Lanes* and *Black Tickets.* A Prix de Medici Estranger and National Book Award finalist, twice an NBCC finalist, she is a member of The American Academy of Arts and Letters and the recipient of Guggenheim, National Endowment for the Arts, Howard, and Rockefeller Fellowships. Her new novel is forthcoming in 2023. www.jayneannephillips.com

Heather Mateus Sappenfield has published two young adult novels, a middle grade novel, and a short story collection. Among her writing's accolades are a MPIBA Reading the West Awards nomination, a Ben Franklin Awards Silver Medal, a Colorado Book Awards Finalist, an Earphones Award, a SOVAS Award, and Audie Awards Finalist. She lives in Vail, Colorado, where she often heads down muddy backroads. Find out more about Heather at https://heathermateussappenfield.com.

Lee Scharf lives in the Shenandoah Valley of Virginia. In the Valley you are either a "come here" or a "been here." Her family is both, if you count Virginia itself from the 1600s while knowing that Native Americans have a different take on who was here first. She writes fact and fiction for her children and grandchildren, caring most of all that we treat each other well, no matter our differences.

Misty Skaggs was born and raised and continues to scratch out a happy living in the hills and hollers of eastern Kentucky. She is a poet and prose writer as well as an essayist and hardcore, barefooted, radical activist. Check out her book *Planted by the Signs*, currently available from Ohio University Presss.

August Tarrier has completed a collection of short stories entitled *I Hold You Harmless*; four stories from the collection have won prizes for short fiction, including the Zoetrope Prize, and the collection was a Finalist for the Mary McCarthy Prize. She is an editor and manuscript consultant who lives in Philadelphia and is currently wrangling a novel entitled *Mother of God.*

Melanie Rae Thon is a recipient of a Fellowship in Creative Arts from The John Simon Guggenheim Memorial Foundation; a Whiting Writer's Award; the Hopwood Award; and two Fellowships from the National Endowment for the Arts. Her books include *The Voice of the River; Silence & Song; Sweet Hearts; In This Light;* and *First, Body.*

Luis Alberto Urrea, a Guggenheim Fellow and Pulitzer Prize Finalist, is the author of eighteen books, winning numerous awards for his poetry, fiction, and essays. His latest novel, *The House of Broken Angels,* was a 2018 NYT Notable Book of the Year. *Goodnight, Irene*, is forthcoming form Little, Brown in January 2023.

Siobhan Wright lives in Baltimore, Maryland. She has worked at Carroll Community College for most of her life and serves as the Division Chair and a Professor of English. She was recently published in *Flash Fiction Magazine* and *The Ekphrastic Review.*

Paula Younger's writing has appeared in many literary journals, including Harper Collins' *52 Stories, The Rattling Wall, The Chicago Tribune's Printers Row Journal, Gay Mag, The Southeast Review*, and forthcoming in *Another Chicago Magazine*. She earned her MFA from the University of Virginia and received the Henry Hoyns and Bronx Writers Center fellowships. She teaches at Lighthouse Writers Workshop.

Editors

Luanne Smith is a native Kentuckian who now lives in Florida. She is recently retired after 30 years of teaching creative writing and film at West Chester University near Philadelphia. Her fiction has appeared in *Puerto del Sol, The Texas Review, Oxford Magazine* and other literary journals and anthologies. She has published poetry and nonfiction as well. Luanne has hosted well-received AWP Conference panels focused on women writers and the challenges women face writing gritty material and bad-ass female characters. She last presented a panel on the double-standard women writers encounter compared to men when writing sexual content. Her most recent book is an anthology she edited for Madville Publishing, entitled *Taboos & Transgressions: Stories of Wrongdoings.*

Bonnie Jo Campbell grew up on a small Michigan farm with her mother and four siblings in a house her grandfather Herlihy built in the shape of an H. She learned to castrate small pigs, milk Jersey cows, and, when she was snowed in with chocolate, butter, and vanilla, to make remarkable chocolate candy. When she left home for the University of Chicago to study philosophy, her mother rented out her room. She has since hitchhiked across the U.S. and Canada, scaled the Swiss alps on her bicycle, and traveled with the Ringling Bros and Barnum & Bailey Circus selling snow cones. As president of Goulash Tours Inc., she has organized and led adventure tours in Russia and the Baltics, and all the way south to Romania and Bulgaria.

Her collection *Women and Other Animals* details the lives of extraordinary females in rural and small town Michigan, and it won the AWP prize for short fiction; her story "The Smallest Man in the World" has been awarded a Pushcart Prize. Her novel *Q Road* investigates the lives of a rural community where development pressures are bringing unwelcome change in the character of the land. Her critically-acclaimed short fiction collection *American Salvage*, which consists of fourteen lush and rowdy stories of folks who are struggling to make sense of the twenty-first century, was a finalist for the 2009 National Book Award in Fiction.

For decades, Campbell has put together a personal newsletter—*The Letter Parade*—and she currently practices Koburyu kobudo weapons training. She has received her M.A. in mathematics and her M.F.A. in writing from Western Michigan University. She now lives with her husband and other animals outside Kalamazoo, and she teaches writing in the low residency program at Pacific University.

CPSIA information can be obtained
at www.ICGtesting.com
Printed in the USA
LVHW020200111S0523
74697272LV00002B/327